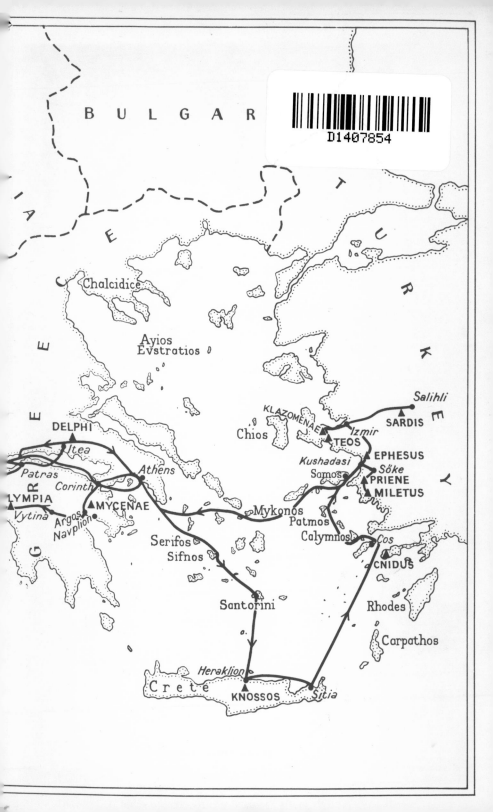

EX
LIBRIS

SAINT
JOSEPH'S
COLLEGE

EAST CHICAGO
INDIANA

Night Sky at Rhodes

Looking across from the Hospital of Asclepios on Cos to the mainland of Asia Minor

NIGHT SKY
AT RHODES

Stephen Toulmin

HARCOURT, BRACE & WORLD, INC
New York

Contents

—◦❧ ❧◦❧⧉❧◦❧ ❧◦—

Illustrations

—◦❧❧◦❧❧◦❧◦❧—

Preface

—◦❦◦❦◦❦◦❦◦❦◦❦◦—

During the spring of 1960, a small academic film unit was in Greece and Turkey, making a film about the beginnings of science. We had gone there with an intense interest in the scientific ideas of the classical Greeks and the conviction that, of all the aspects of the Hellenic achievement, this alone was completely unique. Other cultures and civilizations – French, Etruscan, Japanese, T'ang, Khmer – have had an Aeschylus or a Pheidias, have produced noble dramas or fine sculptures; but the Greeks, and only the Greeks, invented the idea of an abstract and general scientific theory.

Why was this, and how did it come about? We started with these questions; and also with the feeling that, unless one could see them in relation to the life which created them, the literary relics which are our prime evidence about the first systems of scientific ideas must remain just so many words. Possibly this connection could no longer be made; the tenuous threads joining those ideas to the vanished life from which they sprang had – presumably – been snapped by history past hope of reconstruction.

Or had they? That was what we wanted to find out, and this book tells how we set about the task.

1 · The Festival of Santa Ecclisse

—◦❧ ❧ ◦❧ ❀ ❁ ◦❧ ◦ ❧ ◦—

Just beyond Forli the Apennines begin. A dozen miles away on the fringe of the mountains is the Renaissance hill-town of Bertinoro, which served the poet Carducci as his embodiment of the Earthly Paradise. From the neighbouring heights, the hotel-keeper told us, there is a splendid view across the great plain of the Romagna, and here we should see the solar eclipse quite clearly. With his advice in mind, we went early to bed, for the period of totality – at this point only one and a half minutes in length – was due to take place not long after sunrise next day.

The eclipse promised to provide a 'pilot' run for our whole expedition, and would show us something of what we might expect to find later on, when we reached Greece. For, among all the early peoples, no aspect of Nature was more hemmed about with emotions and beliefs – none was more 'ominous' – than the periodic Death and Rebirth of the Sun. Eclipses played a central part (for instance) in the astronomy, the ritual and even the state-craft of ancient Mesopotamia, and the official prognosticators of Babylon became skilled eclipse-forecasters. In the great network of Creation, by which all things in the Heavens and the Earth were bound together, eclipses were portents. The onset of un-natural darkness seemed the shadow of a coming evil, and the only problem was to avert the worst anger of the offended god. Yet had anything of these older ways of thought survived into the Europe of the twentieth century? Was the Sun still a religious object, whose integrity was of vital concern to man? Now we should see.

Happily, the eclipse coincided not only with our arrival in Venice, but also with the end of Carnival and the beginning of Lent – for it would take place just after sunrise on Ash

Wednesday. This conjunction was ambiguous. It could give the eclipse either a frivolous or a penitential character, and in the old days men would have had little doubt which way to take it. The Sun's being extinguished in the early hours of the very first day of Lent would have reinforced the gloomy aspect of the event, and made it doubly ominous. (Remember the traditional association of the Crucifixion with a solar eclipse.) Would this Lent, then, be an occasion for darker penitence and harsher renunciation than usual?

Nothing of the sort – Northern Italy had been enjoying an unusually fine February, and Carnival in Venice was proving, if anything, even gayer than usual. Parties of children in fancy-dress trooped across the Piazza and, far from depressing the gaiety, the eclipse had been swept up into the pre-Lent festivities, serving as a pretext for extending Carnival eight hours past closing-time, by providing a kind of astronomical colophon at the end of Mardi Gras. Having arranged a round trip from Venice into the zone of totality, the enterprising Jugoslav shipping-line was actually managing to secularize the extra hours completely. Passengers would first dance all night on their floating ballroom and later sleep their way homewards, after having – so to speak – 'had the eclipse for breakfast'.

At Forli itself everybody was preoccupied with the forthcoming *spettacolo cosmico*. The newspapers were billing it as a natural counter-attraction to the cinema and the sports arena. The television service was putting on a special programme. Men, women and children were providing themselves with dark glasses – at the very least, with strips of blackened photographic film. In the café, cycling and football were forgotten: for once, the talk was all of space travel, cosmology and the planets. While a determined minority danced Carnival out to the sounds of the Radar Dance Band, the rest of the population was busy mobilizing itself for next morning's special treat. As we ate our supper, the hotel-keeper's six-year-old daughter came over to us with a final warning: 'Do be careful! If you watch the eclipse on television, don't forget – you *must* remember to wear your dark glasses!' So, by half-past seven next morning, we were driving up a lane from the main road towards Bertinoro. Every pull-off and cart-track had its quota of excited families. The road clambered up across the foothills, and swung round in a great arc to the first col: a compact group of medieval buildings crowned the pass, looking like a small piece of Tuscany transplanted across the Apennines. We drove carefully into the crowded town. The main square was packed with motor-coaches. The concluding Act of the Carnival was about to begin.

Just beyond the town were two hills. We followed the signs to the larger, Monte Mai, scrambling up to the hill-top by a short cut. We came out, not on to a bare crest, but into a large court-yard beside a restaurant. '*Us Bev Ben*,' shouted a dialect slogan on the wall, '*Us Magna Mei, Us Ved e Mond*.' We were in no mood for eating and drinking, and all we wanted was to 'see the world'; so we followed the stream of spectators out onto the paved square stretching from the restaurant to the edge of the hill-top. The parapet was crowded. There was all the tension of a great evening at La Scala, and we were in the Upper Circle. All that was left of the sun was squinting at us out of a rapidly-fading back-drop, and the director was clearly going to bring this performance to a split-second climax.

It was already chilly. Early in a mid-February morning we could not very well spare the sun's radiant heat, so we took a quick turn round the *piazzetta*. On three sides the ground fell away sharply, but the fourth was enclosed by the colour-washed wall of the restaurant. As the sunlight faded into the unnatural dusk, all the colours of the plaster were richened and enhanced. But more: there was a brand-new filigree crispness in all the shadows. The last narrow sliver of sun cast onto the plaster a sharp and separate silhouette of every twig and leaf, so that we could see for ourselves – for the first time – how crude and blurred ordinary daylight shadows are. At the far end of the wall, a small path led round to the front of the building. There was just room for a couple of cages, one of them housing three or four doves, the other occupied by two tame monkeys. We watched them a little curiously, remembering the violent and dramatic antics which the Italian newspapers had been warning their readers to expect from animals and birds during the period of totality. ('Their instinctive sensibilities,' it was explained, 'are more highly developed than those of man himself.') We were to be disappointed. A few minutes earlier, the doves had still been cooing, but now they were settling down to sleep, as though the previous sunrise had been some sort of premature illusion: meanwhile, the introverted monkeys remained entirely unmoved, and passed the whole *fenomeno estraordinario* scratching each other abstractedly.

But now the moment of climax was on us. As the last edge of the sun disappeared, a gasp – devoid of all fear or bewilderment – went up from round the *piazzetta*. It was a cry of admiration and astonishment: the curtain was up, the audience had surrendered unconditionally to the spell of the impresario's stagecraft, and the ninety seconds which followed were earning a place in memory alongside a handful of sublimely-sung arias and supremely contrived football-movements. The eclipse was (in short) a Jolly Good Show. From the left-hand side of the Sun there sprang out a fine rosy protuberance; the sky around it was filled, throughout several times its normal diameter, with the pearly light of the corona; but for most of that minute-and-a-half, eyes remained fixed on the coal-black disc which was dominating the celestial stage. Then in a fraction of a second – as though clicked off by a switch – the protuberance and the corona vanished. Like the last triumphant top C crowning a soprano's set-piece, a white-hot arc of light reappeared at the top right-hand corner of the disc, and the audience broke spontaneously into applause. The cosmic spectacle was finished. The next performance in Italy would be staged in A.D. 2081.

The crowd began to break up and flow away towards the exit, like an ice-pack released by the returning sun. One wave surged towards the restaurant (to *bev ben*), another streamed back down the road towards Bertinoro. Carnival was over for another year. The Grand Celestial Coincidence had inaugurated the Forty Days of Lent with a showmanship no one could fault. By a magnificent stroke of timing, a congregation of millions had been drawn together into a solemn act of devotion, and the Mediter-

14

ranean talent for syncretism had done its work. If Dionysius, Saint Liber, Hagia Sophia (and even Es Skob) could be canonized or deified, why should this not also happen – I thought – to a natural phenomenon? For, surely, what we had just experienced was best described as 'the Festival of Santa Ecclisse'. The only pity was that Carnival did not terminate in a solar eclipse every year: in that case, Santa Ecclisse would rapidly become one of the most popular figures in the calendar.

*　　*　　*

Like all the best expeditions, our own had at least two aims: a primary, public purpose which we could be confident of achieving and also a deeper motive, an ideal – probably (even preferably) unattainable. The official business, which brought it within the scope of our work for the Nuffield Foundation, was to collect material for a documentary film about the beginnings of scientific thought in Ancient Greece; and our cabins on the boat from Venice to Athens were jammed with boxes, cases and sharp-pointed packages containing all our film equipment. (We *hoped* that we had arranged beforehand for a painless passage through the Customs at the Piraeus.) Yet we had, behind this official purpose, another wish also: one which looks fanciful when presented in the anaesthetic preservative of one's handwriting, though it can perhaps be *spoken* without blenching: we wanted to discover, to recapture, to reconstruct within ourselves, the mental attitudes of men long dead – the intellectual postures which went to the making of those first scientific ideas.

In this respect the trip was a pure experiment. How it would work out, what light it could possibly throw on Thales and his successors, we simply could not tell beforehand. Would all those tantalizing literary fragments, on which scholars have exercised endless philological ingenuity, still appear as completely opaque when re-read (so to speak) on their native heath? Had the origins and growing-points from which the Greek vision of Nature sprang vanished without leaving any trace? Or should we perhaps recognize, in and around the Aegean Sea, some evidence of the life and experience which nourished those first seedlings of the scientific imagination? Like Crusaders or pilgrims – as in effect we were – we would probably begin by looking for the wrong things, and be distracted from the proper objects of our pilgrimage. There was nothing to do but wait and see.

In both our tasks we were faced by the same basic problems – how to recognize, grasp and express 'intangibles'. In both, we could hope for evidence from two directions – from the people and from their environment. We might possibly find traces of the older ideas still surviving among the Greeks of the present day; but, even if that hope were disappointed, there was still a lot to learn from the country itself – and this, after all, was the matrix within which the life and ideas of Classical Greece took shape.

Before ever starting from England we had faced the first obstacle of all – a certain scepticism springing from the very nature of our basic tasks. This proved most obstinate when we tried to explain to others our ambition to make *films* about ideas, for then the seeming 'intangibility' of our subject presented itself as an insoluble problem. Can one capture ideas in a net, or register them on a film? Will attitudes come to feed out of your hand, or offer themselves to the noose? A single ironical twist of phrase seemed enough to prick the balloon of our hopes, and a dozen impeccable arguments proved that they could not be fulfilled. But irony can be made a substitute for imagination, and deductive arguments may be an excuse for keeping one's feet off all uncertain ground. This radical scepticism – our own as well as other people's – was a challenge which had to be met, but it was not (we decided) a very substantial one. For both the ironies and the arguments relied too much on one single assumption, that ideas are completely *elusive*; and we had a hunch that this assumption could be undermined, since it proved *too much*.

How can you film ideas? How, for that matter, can you film a ghost? You load your camera, turn it towards the spectre, and set it running: when you develop the film, there is nothing to be seen. Are ideas intangible in *that* sense? If so, how is it that you can film *emotions*? (Irony too easily concludes that this is impossible, when Hollywood does it every day.) Of course one cannot equate an emotion with any particular grimace, gesture, or catch of the breath – with any of those things which can be recorded on film or tape. Yet what follows from this? Not that emotions cannot be filmed but, rather, a clearer recognition of the problems actually involved in doing so. Irony dismisses the task by mis-describing it: of course intangibles cannot have their snapshots taken, but why attempt the inconceivable? The director of a theatrical film has a difficult task, but not a downright meaning-less one. His business is to convey the emotions his actors are ex-pressing, by presenting a *calculated selection* of images and sounds in which these emotions are embodied; and a film about ideas must be made on the same principles. The problem is to recognize a sequence of sights and sounds in which the ideas in question are embodied, or by which they can be conveyed. One seeks to evoke understanding by stimulating a kind of intellectual reson-ance.

The truth is that, however intangible ideas may be in them-selves, the situations in which they originate are quite definite and describable, and the effects to which they give rise are often perfectly tangible. Our immediate task, accordingly, was to look for the origins of Greek science in the Aegean environment, and for any enduring effects which that tradition has left on men's ideas. The work of reconstruction had begun at home in the study, reflecting on what scholars had made for us out of the surviving fragments of original text. Now we had to confirm and deepen our interpretations, by exposing ourselves to what-ever remained of the situations in which these speculations germinated. In this respect the two aims of our trip were inter-dependent: our film would convey the ideas of the first Greek scientists convincingly, only if we managed, at least in outline, to recreate *in ourselves* something of the attitudes with which the classical Greeks faced their world.

Once again, then, irony was a refuge for cowardice. To try to read the minds of men who died two thousand years ago by a species of 'historical thought-transference': there was an enter-prise whose silliness stood self-condemned in its very description.

But that was not our plan. Our concern was rather a kind of intellectual archaeology, which might be difficult but could not be ridiculed out of hand. Of course orthodox archaeology still had a seeming advantage over us: all those potsherds and house-floors, bones and weapons – obvious relics, of a kind that a historian of ideas was apparently denied. Yet this contrast could easily be overstated. A man who digs for the sake of 'finds' alone is not an archaeologist but a grave-robber. The archaeologist, as much as the historian of ideas, comes to the relics of the past with questions in mind. His business is to recover and reconstruct not just a valuable bracelet or a beautiful jar but a vanished 'way of life' (the intangibles are not to be denied!), and from that point of view there is nothing particularly out-of-the-way about *intellectual* archaeology – it is only one element in the larger task. The novel theories of nature put forward by the Greeks during the last thousand years before Christ surely had some roots or stimuli in the Aegean way of life. The problem was to know what to look out for.

★   ★   ★

The Greek scientists themselves have provided an image which conveys something of our problem. As we travel North or South, we change the aspect of the Heavens. Familiar constellations drop out of sight, and new configurations of stars dominate the sky. By the time we reach the far side of the globe, few of our old friends are left – and those few are upside down. (There is great persuasiveness in the sight of Orion standing on his head.) The classical Greeks knew this very well, and saw clearly what it implied. Before 350 B.C., it was already a scientific commonplace that the surface of the Earth was spherical, and by Roman times this had become a literary commonplace, too: *Cross the sea*, said Horace, *and you change the sky – but not your state of mind*. From celestial changes, as Posidinius and Eratosthenes recognized, it was not hard to estimate the Earth's circumference. When, in the night sky at Rhodes, a star lay just on the southern horizon, it was observed to reach a height of five degrees at Alexandria;

and when the sun was directly overhead on the Upper Nile, it was still some seven degrees off the zenith at the Delta. By comparing the aspects of the sky at two different places, one could infer their difference in latitude – and so the magnitude of the whole terrestrial sphere.

The inference we should have to make was similar. After two millennia and more, our modern picture of Nature presents us with patterns of ideas quite unlike those of our forefathers and predecessors. Yet has the wheeling vault of Time thrust their constellations entirely below our intellectural horizon? Have we reached a pole so opposed to theirs that *nothing* of the Greek vision of the world can still be seen? Or can we still glimpse, low in the sky, enough of those older configurations for us to plot our relative positions?

If we were to reconstruct these older constellations, this was not going to be an entirely straightforward task. We must find our evidence of the older ways of thought either in Nature or in Man, and – as our experiences at Bertinoro had shown – it was no good expecting too much of Man. Far from shrinking in terror, all the Italians we had seen had thrown themselves whole-heartedly into the business of *enjoying* the eclipse. Having lost its last miasma of superstitious awe, it had become a source of positive pleasure. Evidently the triumph of Newton was complete. Since the year 1687, when his theory of the solar system was published, men's attitudes towards eclipses had been altered irreversibly. Short of an almost unimaginable catastrophe, the age of wailing and gong-beating was over, even in Tashkent and Timbuctoo. It was a very understandable reaction:

> . . . Now we know
> The sharply-veering ways of comets, once
> A source of dread, nor longer do we quail
> Beneath appearances of bearded stars . . .

The astronomers had predicted the eclipse exactly to the second, and the spectators could climb back into their buses and cars, gratified at this evidence of our intellectual command. In this way, the intellectual victories of seventeenth-century astronomy had helped also to liberate us all from fear. Here was something which no one, however anti-scientific his temper, could really afford to despise. No gongs in Bertinoro. . . .

The eclipse was still fresh in our minds three days later, as our ship made its way up the Gulf of Corinth. By midday, she was safely threaded into the needle's-eye of the Corinth Canal, and by three in the afternoon we expected to be alongside at the Piraeus. What should we find when we got there? Among the Italians, older attitudes towards Nature had evidently lost much of their force: would things be any different among the Greeks? Three centuries of modern science (I suspected) would have transformed all their conscious beliefs about the natural world as completely as our own. In their personalities, some traces of their ancestry might remain recognizable; yet we could no longer expect to find them sharing their forbears' own conception of Nature. At best, we should be in for a piece of detective-work, and we could not afford to miss any clues.

2 · The Magnanimous Cretan

—◦❦~◦❦◗❦◦~❦◦—

Bracing his head and feet against the ground, the professional strong-man strained his body up like a bow, the muscles of his stomach pulsating against the enveloping cocoon of ropes and chains. The crowd was hushed and tense. Quick as a cat, he flicked himself round on to his hands and knees: his black knitted tank-crew cap, with the regimental badges sewn on it, flew from his head and fell some feet away into the dust. He rested a moment, his hair over his eyes, panting from the exertion. Then the spasms began once more: rolling, wriggling, his muscles working singly and together, as he probed for the crucial point of weakness in his bonds.

Now one loop of rope was visibly loosening. The crowd stirred. There were shouts of excitement and encouragement: 'Tasso! Tasso!' Mixed among his groans and grunts came single words and phrases – '... mad ... must be mad ... see a *psychiatros* ....'. On the far side of the ring a young soldier in battledress let out a titter. In a flash Tasso was on his feet, radiating pride and scorn. The brass lion-heads on his belt gleamed in the sunset below the brown of his torso. Throwing back his arms as far as the chains would allow, he lobbed taunts towards the soldier, who was doing his best to disappear into the unsympathetic crowd. Then, sweeping the ring of spectators with a look of injured magnanimity, he let fly his last unanswerable plea: '*Mad?*' he cried, '*I may be mad! But at least I speak logically!*'

We were on Philopappos, the hill from which the best-known views of the Acropolis are photographed. Though Roman Catholic Italy was already four days on into Lent, here in the Orthodox zone the religious calendar was still unreformed, and the Greek Carnival was just coming up to the boil. By day,

Athens was a city of kites: great octagons of blue, white and scarlet, with tails of noble length streaming out before the stiff north-easterly breeze. By night, the population surged out into all the public places and tides of humanity blocked the narrow streets of the old city. Now, guided by our friend Herakles, we were making our way up the paved track which leads to the Roman ruins on the summit of Philopappos. *Bouzouki* music was drifting in waves and gusts from a cluster of swings and round-abouts. Capped and belled, a party of mummers were jogging their hobby-horses up the track. Away behind us, stripped of its earlier trees, the grey wall of Hymettus ('*Eemeetos*', Herakles corrected us) hemmed in the sprawling city to landward. And here beside the roadway we came across Tasso, the strong man, strutting and declaiming at the centre of an attentive ring of Athenians.

At first, we did not recognize him for what he was – standing there on a dust-patch in his knitted cap and boots, with the lion-belt holding up a pair of the briefest black cotton shorts. Spare, muscular, grizzled, he kept that noble Greek profile referred to in England, rather mysteriously, by the phrase 'a Roman nose'. But, despite his volubility, what he had to say scarcely sounded like real oratory. (Its general drift – such as it was – came across to us as much by gesture as by word, and Herakles gave us a précis of the rest.) Then suddenly he revealed his special talents. Picking up a log from which two thick nails projected, he lifted it to his mouth and gripped the nails with his teeth: millimetre by millimetre, with a fine show of grunts and grimaces, he pulled them out in turn. There was a round of applause. He made a quick circuit of the crowd with his collecting-box, and then launched himself into another patriotic speech. 'There!' he ended, 'you leave me poor – so poor that I shall have to go and find work in Germany! All my friends have had to go to Germany; but I! . . .' he paused for effect – '*Eimi Kritikos! I am a Cretan!*'

'National character' is something about which we can easily, and understandably, be sceptical. Surely (we may feel) all the peoples of modern Europe have more in common with each

22

other than any one of them has with its own ancestors. Exposed to the same influences, living similar lives, operating the same machines, even eating the same breakfast cereals, how could they *fail* to be alike? And what possible reason could there be for them to resemble men and women who have been dead for centuries?

This argument is difficult to counter – except that its conclusion is so often contradicted by experience. To this day, the languages of Europe preserve untranslatable epithets, which express each people's ideals of life and character – *sympathique*, *gemütlich*, level-headed, *megalopsychos* – and the Greek language is specially full of such words. A *philotimos* man is not 'ambitious' as we in England know ambition, nor a *philoxenos* one 'hospitable' merely in our sense. Such personal epithets do not reflect bald, objective properties, like shape or weight, but spring from conceptions of life and humanity whose whole pattern varies from nation to nation; and tradition can preserve those conceptions alive for generations.

A Greek, for instance, sees his obligations above all as matters of self-respect: they are not for him, as they are for some other peoples, burdens imposed by others. As his life unfolds, the situations which he encounters give rise to these obligations, and he is impelled to act as they require because otherwise he will feel self-dishonoured. Does this mean that he will feel 'ashamed'? No: for once again the English word has quite irrelevant implications. The hang-dog or sneaking expression typical of 'shame', in our sense, springs from a fear of other people's disapproval. But a Greek is driven by a fiercer motive – the disapproval he fears is *his own*. One result of this enhanced sense of obligations is that conflicts of duties become sharper; and this helps to create the flavour of moral comedy characteristic of Greek life.

An Oxford friend of mine happened to visit an Athenian pupil just as he was about to return to his native island for the christening of his infant son. By a sheer coincidence, my friend was scheduled to go to the same island by the same boat. This being a serious landmark in the Athenian's life, *philotimia* demanded that he should travel – and be seen to travel – first-class on the boat:

this was something he owed to himself. The English don, however, was unwilling to pay the price of a first-class ticket, and could not bring himself to accept one from his pupil as a gift. He was fully determined to go second-class. This put the Athenian in a quandary: piety and *philoxenia* now forbade him to leave his teacher without a guide and companion, and imposed on him the obligation of sharing the second-class cabin. How was the quandary to be resolved? A way quickly suggested itself. He boarded the ship by the first-class gangway, together with his wife and child, and installed them in a first-class cabin; next, he returned to the ship's rail, and waved goodbye to his enthusiastic relatives; finally, he ducked down below the ship's rail, out of sight of the quay, and crept round to the second-class cabins to fulfil his obligations as host. On arrival at the island, he reversed the procedure. And all this was done, not in order to 'show off' or 'maintain status' or 'keep face' (all of them profoundly un-Hellenic conceptions), but merely as things which he felt he had to do, if he was to go on happily living with himself.

* * *

So there we were on Philopappos Hill, little more than twenty-four hours ashore, and already being presented with a perfect illustration of that fundamental Greek virtue, *megalopsychia*. Tasso was certainly poor, but he was also proud; and yet he avoided that vicious haughtiness which the English associate with 'pride'. Rather, he was conscious of his proper position as an individual, as a Cretan, as a Greek, as a man – above all, as a man who had kept himself in good shape, and who did his best, even in adversity, to think and talk rationally. In the great days of Greece, Aristotle had classified man as the animal most clearly differentiated from others by his essential rationality. Now in these lesser days, whatever circumstances might do to one, that rationality was still worth clinging to. 'A fool, but a rational fool': there could be worse epitaphs. (Echoes of Pascal.) Through Tasso's concern for 'logic' and 'speaking rationally', there shone the central spark of Aristotle's personal ideal – the 'big-souled'

24

man, whose *megalopsychia* continues to defeat both the English language and the English imagination.

During our first weeks in Athens we came across similar traces of the old Hellenic personality. In my notes I find the following:

Athens – February 20. Well, hope springs eternal . . . we have been in Greece less than two days, and already the temptation – or the hope, if it is not too delusive – is springing up again. We are clearly not going to get an unobstructed view of Nature, whether through the eyes of the ancient Greeks or through our own, for one thing is already obvious: in Greece, Man is very much in the centre of the picture, and Man here means something recognizably related to the earlier Greeks. Recognizably? That I suppose begs the question, but I said the temptation was already growing up, and there it is.

We have already met, on the quay itself, one man whose behaviour has fanned our latent spark of conviction that somewhere – away from the neon and sophistication of Greater Athens – we may find our clues to the intellectual traditions of ancient Greece. For a few minutes (such is the instinctive Hellenic sense of proportion) he even succeeded in distracting our attention from the noble wreckage of the Parthenon. Here, we see, Man remains the measure of all things. . . . Despite the grandeur of the scenery, the works of Man are not dwarfed by overhanging crags as they are in Switzerland: the landscape is still aptly proportioned to human beings, and individual humans still form the centre of the picture. True enough: a genuinely Homeric argument developed, once we got into the Customs shed and tried (it being Saturday afternoon) to get our £4,000 worth of apparatus cleared through without delay.

The Customs Officer was determined to be wooed like Achilles. Granted – our friend Gregory had come down from the Prime Minister's office to vouch for us. Granted – Gregory had brought with him all the 'permissions' for our filming, together with the detailed list of apparatus we had forewarned him that we would be bringing. Granted – our intentions were, without doubt, honest and straightforward. All the same, there were some other facts to be considered: it was, after all, Saturday afternoon, and the next two days were Carnival holidays. So we had better come back on Tuesday, leaving the equipment in their scrupulous custody until then. If that did not satisfy us, then at any rate it was necessary to prove that, in a matter of Customs procedure, the Prime Minister's office had any *locus standi.* And as for all these documents (*po, po, po . . .*), these permissions and lists, what was their relevance? And what good was a list of equipment written in *English*?

Gregory and Herakles, with June acting as back-stop, pursued a two-pronged chess attack against these argumentative pawns. Meanwhile, I was able to get the car out of bond in no more than half the time: having done my part, I stood back until the moment came for signing the final documents, and watched the scene with some pleasure. ('What's the Greek for "torque-motor" and "400-foot magazine"?') So long as things kept moving, it was gratifying to see how his own proper pride kept the Customs Officer in play, for as long as honourable defensive moves remained open to him. It had its irritating side, no doubt, but it was all extremely *reasonable* – quite unlike the brute unreasoning obstinacy of Spanish officials. The man had a spark of individuality which commanded respect; and a self-regard which he rightly indulged, for this self-regard is an essential part of the foundation on which democracy stands firm. Men must be prepared to maintain their positions until cogently argued out of them, and never be excessively submissive – surrendering their interests without being given adequate reasons for doing so. Anyway, we had all afternoon. . . .

A few days later, a formal call of respect on F. – the well-known poet with a high position in the National Tourist Organization – plunged us into a scene from Sophocles. We were sitting briefly in the ante-room, waiting to be introduced into the august presence, when there came a crimson roar of fury from the inner office, and for one instant our host appeared in the doorway thundering like an affronted bull. A moment later, the door slammed again, and half-a-minute passed before we were invited within. How well one knows the smooth solicitude which would mask the face of a British official placed in a similar situation! There was no such falsity about F. A purple thundercloud hung over all the civilities of our courtesy call, and whatever the cause of his wrath (which we never discovered) the last lightning-flashes of emotion were still visible in the fluctuating expressions of his face. Here was not the sulking of Achilles, but the true unbridled indignation of Ajax.

Not that we made such identifications as these too hurriedly – we knew better than that. After all, when Jules Dassin made his

26

film *Never on Sunday*, he had a real point. To go around twentieth-century Greece, seeing everybody as personifying the admirable features of the old Hellenic culture, would merely be silly. Everyday life in Greece today is not lived on a Homeric or Sophoclean level – nor was it in Homer's or Sophocles' day, either. At the same time, Dassin's film (we found) had deeply offended our own Greek film-making friends: their fellow-countrymen were not Homeric, they conceded, but nor were they naïvely frivolous. While they could not personify the old Greek virtues, they were not wholly devoid of them; the consciousness of their traditions could still preserve in them a concern with balance and seriousness that *Never on Sunday* conspicuously lacked.

(Greek national character seemed, in fact, likely to survive longer even than the Greek alphabet. For whether that could last much longer we already had reason to doubt. By now, all the signposts are duplicated, and only a few of the imported goods in the shops carry any but 'Latin' labels. Some European firms–Dutch and German particularly–take the trouble to Hellenize their trade-marks, so that ΦΑΦΦ [Pfaff] sewing machines advertise their merits alongside ΦΙΛΙΠΣ [Philips] – and ΜΠΛΑΥΠΟΥΝΚΤ [Blaupunkt] electrical equipment; but the big international oil companies, conscious of an economy larger than Switzerland's – let alone that of Greece – make no such concessions. 'Shell' and 'Mobil' are international words, which the Greeks must jolly well learn to recognize for themselves. Until quite recently, of course, Greece was on the very fringe of the Romanized world, with Bulgaria to the North using the Cyrillic, and Turkey to the East, the Arabic script. But Ataturk has, so to speak, outflanked the Greek alphabet, and it is in danger of becoming, fifty years hence, a mere oddity or affectation–like the Erse alphabet of present-day Ireland.)

As time went on, we came to appreciate better the reasons why our friends disliked *Never on Sunday*. Dassin had done as much – and as little – for Greece as Daninos has done for England with his stories about 'Major Thompson'; which are best-sellers in other countries, but not in England itself. Both remain entangled in externals. In externals, of course, Athens has been transformed.

The new office-blocks in the centre of the city would be equally in place at Cleveland or in Brussels. Greek car-drivers have an individualistic variety of fast badness, which is quite distinct from the wavering obstructiveness of English and the Gadarene recklessness of Italians; but a congested street is a congested street the world over. As for the southern suburbs of Athens, along the sea-shore, these are rapidly acquiring a strong flavour of San Francisco Bay. A double-track motorway now leads out from Phaleron past the international airport, to end at Vouliagmeni, on the far outskirts.

It was there that Herakles took us for dinner our first evening ashore, in a brand-new restaurant straight off Fisherman's Wharf: a split-level building, with long, low picture-windows on three sides, furnished with unstained woodwork, thick dark carpets and tanks full of fish and water-plants – impeccable contemporary taste, but entirely cosmopolitan. The place had been open only a fortnight, and the dandies of Athens were still catching up with it. Soft lights beside each table glinted back from the dew on shining ice-buckets. One thing alone was out-of-tune in this transatlantic picture: the napkin-shrouded bottles in the ice-buckets contained not champagne but beer – the ubiquitous 'Fix', introduced to Greece a century ago by an enterprising Bavarian brewer called Fuchs, and still the snob drink. (Wine is for peasants.)

Yet even the vogue for novelties is, I suppose, not new: Paul of Tarsus remarked on it. If the gardens and fences of Athens overflowed with hibiscus and bougainvillea rather than with anemones or asphodel, that too was only to be expected. My own English taste for wild flowers led me to hope that somewhere in Attica I should find the orange crocus growing wild. I asked Herakles about this, but he could not help me. The very word *krokos* meant nothing to him, and my lame descriptions left him still in the dark. Using a mixture of French, dumbshow and single Greek words, I explained what I was after to his fiancée: she confirmed (*oui, oui*) that such flowers existed, but was evidently baffled by my interest in them – '*Il n'y a rien d'extraordinaire là-bas.*' I dropped the subject: eccentricity is largely a

28

matter of geography, and there was no point in appearing too eccentric at the very beginning of our collaboration. (Come to that, I must appear to them rather like the Indian Maharajah who went to great expense in order to keep clumps of dandelions growing in his palace courtyards.)

★   ★   ★

For the moment, too, our interest in Greek science would have to wait. We should find no wild crocuses growing in the centre of Athens, nor any mule tracks, nor any ancestral memories of Thales and Aristotle. In the city, at any rate, these were certainly overgrown by bougainvillea, and parkways, and ideas drawn from modern science. By the end of two weeks' formalities, we were impatient to be off into the country. Fotis, the young Greek who was coming with us as cameraman, had checked and tested all our equipment. We had our first batch of filming ready planned, and were anxious to get into the mountains of the Peloponnese before the last snows melted. Away from the automobiles and international architecture of Athens, we were convinced, things were to be found more important for our purposes than crocuses and mule tracks.

Before we left the city, however, we did have one evening with a real flavour of things to come. We drove into Athens along the great, five-mile boulevard up from Phaleron, which carries you in a straight line all the way from the sea to a point near the foot of the Acropolis. The view ahead is dominated by the needle-point of Lykabettos, and the buildings on either side, growing progressively taller as one nears the city centre, are bright with neon signs – half of them in Latin script, half of them in Greek. Then, as we went towards the centre of the city, we plunged into a different world – the *Plaka*. Had they been deserted, the streets would still have been tortuous: overflowing with the Carnival crowd, they were near-impassable. Before the epoch of the insatiable automobile, Mediterranean towns reacted to the fierceness of summer by shrinking themselves tight together, the shady canyons of their streets providing a defence against the

29

violent sun. So here, clinging to the skirts of the Acropolis, the older quarters of Athens form a jumble of narrow streets, at once disordered and full of character. In late February, the weather was as cold as it ever gets. Along the edge of the pavement there were dozens of barrows, each carrying a small charcoal stove (known as a *foufou*) loaded with hot chestnuts. Everywhere we looked, the air was filled, or so it seemed, with multicoloured snow: pink, green, blue, yellow, red and white, the tight handfuls of confetti slowly unfolded, to sift and flutter down into the hair and faces of the crowd.

Herakles guided us along a back street, through a narrow gate, and into a courtyard. Along two sides of a square, lights shone from a single-storey building. Out of a door there drifted steam and tobacco-smoke, and the first tentative notes of a bouzouki. 'Come along in,' he said, looking round the already-crowded *taverna*. 'It's only half-past-eight, so the place is still quite empty.' We sat at a plain wooden table. Round the walls, there were rough murals, showing the chestnut-sellers, tavern-keepers, and other familiar characters of the *Plaka*. The rich fug surrounding us gradually became thicker and hotter; the three musicians played and sang more and more warmly; and meanwhile (for once, how unlike Piccadilly or San Francisco) the unfamiliar dishes succeeded one another – fish-roe, sheep's-guts, stuffed vine-leaves, grilled ribs of lamb, all lubricated by an unlimited quantity of resin-flavoured wine and soda-water.

Soon there was nowhere left to sit down. Yet people continued to push their way between the crowded tables, talking to friends, singing, shouting, hopefully offering for sale either oysters, or newspapers, or pistachio-nuts, or confetti, or rolls of coloured streamers. By ten o'clock, there was a pulse in the atmosphere, as a dozen different parties responded to the rhythm of the music and each other's excitement. Faster and faster, the paper streamers lifted themselves into the air, and lightly uncoiled. One by one, they rose and fell, criss-crossing and knitting themselves across the tables, binding hosts and guests, friends and strangers alike, into a single multi-coloured web. Strangers (it seemed) particularly . . . was this, I wondered, the origin of that Australian custom, of binding a departing ship to the quay-side by hundreds of streamers, each one joining a passenger to a friend on shore, so that a last material bond still links them together, even after the ship has drawn away from the quay? . . . Then it finally became clear to us that our own table was becoming the focus of the streamers. *Philoxenia* evidently takes many forms.

Out in the square, the human flood was reaching the ultimate point of congestion. There was a sort of simmering gaiety, free of drunkenness and rowdiness. (The Greek sense of tragedy and dishonour remains near the surface, even during Carnival.) On the street corners there stood groups of policemen, just in case the simmering flood boiled over for once. A solitary police car stood on the far side of the square, its occupant – a New-York-style cop – nursing a white truncheon on his knee, and humming to himself. Was Greece then a 'police state'? Maybe so; but this was not evidence. As we picked our way across the current of the human tide, towards the street where we had left the car, we turned a corner where three earnest-looking constables stood guard. Pulling ourselves together, we put on an air of good behaviour, and marched straight ahead. Suddenly, the middle policeman drew something out of his pocket, and aimed it at us – a gun? No – a truncheon? Not even a pencil and notebook; but a vast handful of coloured confetti, which he dashed into our eyes, noses and mouths. Silting down over our chins and round our necks, the fragments of paper became inextricably entangled inside our coats and shirts and underwear. Was this too a manifestation of *philoxenia*? If so, it was only the mildest foretaste of what was to come.

3 · Landscape with Fauns

—◦❧◦⟡◦⟡◦⟡◦⟡◦❧◦—

So much for our first look at Hellenic Man: now for Nature. When a solid clue turned up at last, it was from Nature that it came, and it took the form of a revelation. By this I do not mean anything specially dramatic. I suppose the word 'revelation' tends to carry with it the idea of thunderclaps, of the heavens opening – of a 'change of heart', as well as a change of view – whereas in our own case these further associations are beside the point. Still, a 'change of view' there certainly was; and this did something to justify our hope of feeling our way back to the roots from which the Greek view of Nature sprang. The change was, in its own way, quite sudden – like the drawing back of a curtain. Our vision (it seemed) had been fogged by a false assumption. Now the fog lifted.

To state the basic trouble quaintly: *we can't help seeing with our own eyes*. From our standpoint in twentieth-century Western Europe, we are separated from the first Greek philosophers by more than one thousand miles and two thousand years. Their doctrines reach us out of context, in the form of sentences – in many cases fragments of sentences – on the printed page. Naturally enough, we read them and try to understand them just as though they had been written nearer to our own time and place, and apply to these printed words the literary and scientific techniques we have learned in our experience of the science and literature of modern Europe. No other natural starting-point presents itself.

To cite the crucial example: many of the classical Greek philosophers shared a belief in a doctrine which European translators were later to call 'the theory of the four elements'. The difficulty is to decide how such a 'theory' should be interpreted. The doctrine was first formulated clearly in the years round 460 B.C., by a very curious character named Empedocles. One of the few clear things about Empedocles is this: he would never have been elected a Fellow of the Royal Society. We do have a few facts about his life: for instance, that he was a Greek, neither of the mainland nor of the Asiatic coastline, but of Sicily, and we also know (though only roughly) when he lived. When and where he died remains mysterious: he left his home city of Acragas on the South coast of Sicily, to go (it was said) to a conference at Olympia in the Peloponnese – very much as a man might set out from Denmark to go to a NATO meeting in Paris. Did he die while in Greece? . . . or later, on his return journey, while visiting one of the new colonies in Italy? Did he end his life in banishment? . . . or, as a subsequent legend declared, by leaping into the crater of Etna? The last story is almost certainly an invention. For Empedocles was not only a rational thinker and a practical politician, but also a bit of a thaumaturge or 'medicine-man'. Like the Pythagoreans in the nearby Italian colonies, he taught something more than a vision of the natural world; he offered also a way of life involving salvation through purification. Thus he acquired a reputation as a healer:

Straightway, whenever I enter into the flourishing towns, is reverence done me; they go after me in countless throngs, asking of me what is the way to gain; some desiring oracles, while some, who for many a weary day have been pierced by the grievous pangs of all manner of sickness, beg to hear from me the word of healing.

Empedocles would have been exceptional among the great teachers and healers of the classical Mediterranean if marvellous legends had *not* grown up, both about his extraordinary powers and – more especially – about the manner of his death.

Coming so soon after the philosopher-poet Parmenides (a native of Elea, on the Italian coast south of Salerno), Empedocles also found it natural to present his ideas in verse. So the first surviving reference to the four basic material ingredients of the world comes in his poem *On Nature*:

C   33

Hear first the four roots of all things: shining Zeus, lifebringing Hera, Aidoneus, and Nestis whose teardrops are a well-spring for mortals.

As so often among the Greeks, the powers and forces operating in Nature were here personified and given the names of gods; and at this point the classical scholars take over. Who were Nestis and Aidoneus? And how are we to identify these four divinely-named 'roots' with the familiar materials of the natural world? Nestis, they say, was a traditional Sicilian water-goddess: one may guess that her teardrops stand for Water, which forces its way up from a spring like tears from the corner of an eye. As for the other three divinities, scholars have never agreed which exactly is which. We can be confident only that, taken together, the four gods are to be associated with the raw materials of the Sun, the earth, the sky and the sea. 'All of these,' Empedocles goes on to say, 'are at one with all their parts, that are cast far and wide from them in mortal things.' We recognize the basic materials most typically when they are concentrated to form the Sun, the earth, the sky or the sea: in all other things, they are first united together in harmonious combinations by the agency of Love ('They call her also by the names of Joy and Aphrodite'), and later they fall apart again –

At one time all the limbs that are the body's portion are brought together by Love in blooming life's high season; at another, severed by cruel Strife, they wander each alone by the breakers of life's sea.

But here, perhaps, we should switch hats. We can look at Empedocles' poem, not as classical scholars only, but as scientists also. In that case, we may soon find ourselves echoing the questions put so forcibly by Robert Boyle's *Sceptical Chymist*: why just four elements? If we once go beyond Thales' first idea, that all things are composed of one single, universal substance, why stop at *four*? Why not look for thirty (say), or ninety, or even more? In any case: before we start laying down the law about the number of elementary substances, it is surely necessary, first, to collect some experimental evidence. What carefully controlled experiments did Empedocles put forward in support of his own theory, that the number of the fundamental chemical elements is neither more nor less than four? The very question is rhetorical, for the answer is, undeniably: None. And, when once this has been admitted, a sneaking suspicion ought to begin nagging at us. For, if Empedocles appears to come badly out of this interrogation, is that his fault, or ours? Are we asking him the right – that is to say, the relevant – questions, or are we missing his point?

*　　*　　*

At the time, our first two weeks in Greece seemed like months: months tied by the heel to a city which had little to offer us, when all the while we wanted to be off into the mountains, or away through the islands to Asia Minor. In retrospect, of course, our fortnight of courtesy-calls, of preparations, checking, testing and listing, was both necessary and well-spent; and, with the cloudy, chilly weather we were having, we could in any case have done little useful filming earlier. For this was the Greek Spring – *grey spring*, as Hesiod called it some twenty-seven centuries ago – and grey it still is. The land of Greece, according to the travel-posters, has three hundred sunny days a year: many of the other sixty-five, as we now discovered, come in the Spring. During these first weeks, it was frequently overcast, with a north-easter biting its way down from the Black Sea and the Russian steppes, and we made our plans for the first trip out of Athens with some uncertainty of the outcome.

Our route was to be roughly that followed by the travel agents' Four-day Classical Tour – Corinth, Mycenae, up and over Arcadia to Olympia, then by ferry across the gulf to Itea, and back to Athens by way of Delphi. We should have preferred, if possible, to get a little further off the well-worn route, but a look at the map showed that we had little choice. There simply is only this one serious motor-road across the centre of the Peloponnese at all: we might work outwards from it on either side, but we could scarcely avoid going along it. As our first main destination, therefore, we picked on Vytina, a small town

35

right in the centre of the peninsula. Somewhere nearby, with a little luck, we should find the snow and streams we needed in order to illustrate Thales' first speculations about water being *the underlying substance of all things.*

Then, by a blessed coincidence, the weather suddenly cleared up. On the morning we were due to leave Athens we found, to our delight, that the grey overcast had gone. All the reputed brilliance of colour had come back once more into the landscape. Murmuring the expedition's propitiatory motto, *This is Not a Holiday,* we got into the car and set off. Fotis was going ahead independently with three colleagues, in order to do some other filming at Nauplion for one of the Greek government departments. We promised to meet them there early in the afternoon. But that was not how the day worked out, for several different things were lying in wait to distract us. Barely five miles out of Athens, feelings of cultural obligation brought us to a halt at the famous Byzantine Church of Daphni. While we were inside admiring the mosaics of the dome, Fotis and company passed us in their blue Volkswagen van. After twenty minutes we went on, rounded the cement-works of Eleusis, turned left at the main fork where the trunk-roads to the North and South of Greece diverge, towards Megara, and then along the narrowing neck of land which points like an arrowhead aimed at Corinth. Here the olive groves of Attica are squeezed more and more narrowly towards the sea: beyond a certain point, one is traversing along the very flank of a mountain-ridge which falls without interruption into the waters of the Saronic Gulf. According to the ancient legend, this road was the haunt of a brigand called Sciron, who terrorized the region by tossing unco-operative travellers down from the track onto the rocky seashore below, until the hero Theseus came that way and killed him. (Was Theseus in fact – one wonders – the man who exorcized the demons of the mountain, by converting a slippery footpath into a safe bridle-track?) Even in our own day, though this road alone links the two halves of mainland Greece, we found it by no means easy driving. At one point, a large transport truck was jammed in the ditch at the side of the road; and further on, near the Kaki Scala (or Bad Steps), there was wreckage below the road, where a car had recently run over the edge and fallen on to the Scironian Rocks.

When, half-way along this dramatic stretch of highway, we pulled into a lay-by and got out to look at the view, we had other things on our minds rather than Greek Science; but the moment we did so, June and I both remarked on the very same thing. For the whole previous fortnight, the sky, sea and air of Greece had been muddled together in that familiar, blurred amalgam we know in England as 'weather'. Now, suddenly, this muddy mixture had crystallized out into sharply distinct ingredients. Why did the first scientists describe the World as a kind of four-tiered layer cake? We now had only to *look and see*, in order to be struck by the answer to that question: because *that is just what it was like*. The four elements – though 'elements', with its nine-teenth-century echoes of John Dalton's chemistry, is really not the best word – the four 'roots', then, about which Empedocles versified, were all displayed to us directly, one above the other, crisp and clean. Instead of merging together into a fuzzy blur, they had now 'separated out' – and that phrase, which recurs like a refrain in the scientific speculations of the first Greek philosophers, at last explained itself as well.

It was a typical Greek day. This was how the world would normally have presented itself to the Greeks, in 500 B.C. as much as today. Above everything else was the Sky, the home of the Sun and the other shining ones: it was already bright with a glitter that carried the promise of summer fire to come. The region below the sky was the Air: now that the cold rains of Spring had paused for the while, this was at last displaying some-thing of its natural warmth. South across the Gulf lay the rugged mass of the Peloponnese: rough, hard, enduring, dark and massive against the Sun. And in between there lay the lively, glittering water, its waves bright from a million reflected Suns, the intervening depths clear to the very sea-bed, looking from a height as though it were all lifted up – as though the entire sea were lying delicately over the land, without quite touching it. 'Good Lord!' I exclaimed, 'What evidence did Empedocles have for his theory – for his "hypothesis"? What evidence did he *need* to have? Hypothesis? . . . there was nothing hypothetical, or theoretical, about his starting-point: *just look!*'

The Greek philosophers, as one must allow, were surely working their way in the direction of scientific 'theories' and 'hypotheses', as we now know them. In its extreme form, if treated as an all-embracing generalization, Empedocles' doctrine certainly became, in effect, a theory or hypothesis. But he reached that speculative extreme only by working outwards from a starting-point which was not at all speculative. Matter exists in four typical and distinct states – solid, liquid, vapour and fiery (or radiant) – and these are somehow mingled or united into more complex forms. To the classical Greeks the existence of these four primary types or conditions of matter was not merely an uncertain and speculative theory, introduced to explain other, better-established data: it was a manifest fact, which would itself have to be explained in due course. The Greeks might account for the properties of the four 'roots' by relating them together in a kind of taxonomic classification (as Aristotle did), relying on their fundamental properties to display their likenesses and differences. They might guess (as Plato did) that the everyday, macroscopic differences between natural things reflected mathematical contrasts between the shapes of their unobservably minute atoms. Or again, they might regard the four familiar types of matter (as Empedocles himself seems to have done) as the ultimate units – irreducible, and requiring no further explanation. The one choice *not* seriously open to them was to question the existence of the four roots.

As for the other half of Empedocles' doctrine, that in complex bodies the four basic elements are blended, a hundred familiar facts confirmed it: many comparatively solid bodies (for instance) had some liquid in them, most air and vapour contained some specks of solid, and so on. Given Empedocles' starting-point, experimental evidence – carefully controlled, collected and collated – was the last thing he required; for, as we could now see for ourselves, the World was exactly as he described it, with the four basic types (or conditions) of matter separated out, each to its own natural level. Evidently, if we were to set about understanding the natural philosophy of the Greeks, it was a mistake always to be scrutinizing their doctrines with logical spyglasses designed to deal with modern scientific theories. Rather, the thing to do was to see the world *through their eyes*.

* * *

Dr Johnson's friend Edwards tried his hardest to live and think like a philosopher; but despite all his efforts, he explained, 'Cheerfulness keeps breaking in'. From this point on, our expedition into the Peloponnese began to lose its high intellectual tone: Humanity kept breaking in. Though we did not realize it, we had been playing leapfrog with Fotis all the way down the road to Argos and Nauplion. When we looked into the church at Daphni, when we came without warning across the knife-slit of the Corinth canal (right in the middle, as it seemed, of rural Berkshire), when we stopped at the town of Corinth for a snack which elongated itself into lunch: at how many points had we overtaken one another? We crossed the pass below the skyscraper pinnacle of the ancient Corinthian Acropolis, and wound our way down into the orange-groves of the Argolid - a miniature San Joaquin valley, presided over by the ruins of Mycenae; but by the time we had turned left in Argos and along the shore-line road past Tiryns, to reach our destination at Nauplion, it was already the middle of the afternoon. When, about four o'clock, we finally located our hotel, Fotis and his team had been and gone before us, and were already about the town on their own business.

We drove right round the little port all of three times, crossing and re-crossing the trail without actually meeting them, before we gave up. Yes: they had been to the canning-factory, but they had finished and gone away. No: they hadn't been seen at the school. Yes: the policeman on point-duty had seen a blue Volkswagen, but that had been some time ago. As we came round for the third time, the drinkers in the main square lifted their eyes from their glasses of *ouzo*, and broke off their conversations - no Italian shouts or catcalls, of course, yet enough to awaken our

English fear of appearing conspicuous. So we set out on foot, to explore the charming nineteenth-century town for ourselves, and half-past six had come before the human thunderstorm broke irrevocably over our heads.

Not one of the four men was, to the outsider's eye, 'a typical Greek'. Fotis mixes in his ancestry Crete, Macedonia and Russia: square, broad-shouldered, gentle, strong, he shows his conflicting parentage chiefly in his head – the splendid Hellenic profile quarrelling with fair wavy hair. Alec, his chief technical assistant (who owned the van and much of the equipment) we had met briefly before: dark, short, jolly, joking, his egg-shaped head is beginning to go bald and is adorned with a Clark Gable moustache. His brother-in-law, Coulis, had come along for the ride: slighter, with frizzy brown hair and a diffident manner, he clumped around in rubber boots and said little. That leaves the prime character of the quartet, Fotis' camera-assistant, George. In his idiosyncratic way, no doubt, George is as conscientious and devoted a craftsman as Fotis – who treats every piece of apparatus like a mother handling her new-born child – but, whereas Fotis is infinitely predictable and straightforward, George's personality is a continual battle-ground between fantasy and gentle melancholy. Tall and thin, he has the mobile, almost concave face of a sophisticated clown, for whom life exists only as a succession of tragi-comic acts. Yet, though he gives the impression of acting – of 'putting on an act' – this impression is almost certainly mistaken. The variety show is, so to speak, putting itself on within him, with the parts he appears to be playing taking possession of him one after another, like the secret day-dreams of Walter Mitty.

They swept us in a group down to the quayside and into a *taverna*. It was the familiar whitewashed shoe-box of a room, decorated only with an old mirror and some gaudy cheesecake calendars. The furniture comprised a dozen plain wooden tables surrounded by upright wooden chairs, with a charcoal brazier at the back, surrounded by panniers of fresh fish and stuffed tomatoes. We selected our fish, took possession of a table, and relaxed into a mixture of basic English, bad French and monosyllabic Greek. For one evening, without any conscious treaty, gravity was suspended – not the physical influence (of course) but that pervasive gravity or seriousness which, as surely as an electric field of force, penetrates and directs all Greek life. Tacitly shielded from its influence within a metallic screen of deliberate gaiety, the quartet set themselves down for three hours to the hospitable task of diverting us.

Three weeks before, on our way to Venice, we had spent a night at Garda, and had been blasted out of the hotel dining-room by the only other occupants – four men from Milan who launched themselves full-throatedly into an impromptu operatic recital. That had been a terribly earnest affair: a matter of volume, expression and voice-production, with deep emotion simulated by noisy sobs – to put it in our bloody-minded Anglo-Saxon way, a lot of showing-off. At Nauplion, the performance was repeated with one important difference: vocal expression was replaced by facial expression, passion by parody. We began in chorus, but George's internally generated drama gradually began to dominate us – not through any exhibitionism, but simply for its merits as entertainment. Bit by bit, the fantasy elaborated itself within him; and, as he mimed the mad scene from *Lucia di Lammermoor*, his eyes expanded wider and wider, until they were staring out of his long pale face like those of Maria Callas.

Soon the fantasy became collective. Out on the dark street and along the quayside, the air was fresh but no longer cold. Now the entertainment began to play itself not just through the person of George, but through the whole quartet. Round the corner in a small square, a short flight of steps led up to a raised platform. Callas (the nickname imposed itself) vaulted lightly onto the centre of the stage, with the supporting characters grouped neatly behind. Then the mood switched, and we were swept up into a folk-dance down the middle of the street. Another switch, and a broom left by a house door became a hockey stick. Switch again, and Callas the matador was playing Fotis the bull. Click – they were bicycle-racing. Click – they were a team of footballers. . . . Dazed by hours of unmalicious laughter, we fell into bed at the hotel, leaving instructions for them to wake us at six.

41

We had a reason for rising early. For 3,000 years before their sudden flowering in Greece, the seedling habits of social life had been establishing themselves in the vast empires of the Middle East, as in the regimented environment of a nursery-garden. In learning to control the waters of the great rivers, men learned also to control themselves; yet even so all their achievements – and their vision of Nature also – were dominated by the supreme power of the Sun. His was the power that dictated the course of the year, and many of the chances of human life: He could be either a decisive ally or an irresistible enemy. The fortunes of the world were so largely his work that each day's sunrise became a symbol of the Creation – 'In the beginning the Great God appeared in glory on a hill . . .' – just as surely as an eclipse was an omen of evil. Now at Nauplion we had a chance to kill two birds with one stone. Fotis was insistent that we should not miss seeing the fortress of Palamedes, which rings the last mountainous crest where the bare skeleton of the Peloponnese meets the sea; and sunrise would be an excellent time to see it.

There are two ways up to the fort, whose machicolated battlement reaches into the very heart of the town. One can climb directly to the fortress on foot, up the face of the rock, by a stairway which reputedly contains 999 steps – though the more prosaic guide-book trims the number to 857. (The previous evening, Helen, our secretary, had resolutely set off alone to scale the rock by this path. As she climbed, each alternate turn of the stairway brought her back within sight of a group of workmen, who were repairing the road past the foot of the rock: every time she reached another corner, paused and set off up the next flight, they waved and cheered her on more enthusiastically.) Alternatively one can take the road North for a mile out of the town, climbing gradually inland up to a low col, from which a stony track hairpins back along the hill-crest to the rear of the fortress. This was the route we took now. We left the car beside the rugged postern gate, and came out beyond it into the first of the spreading courtyards which lie between the battlements linking the seven distinct sub-forts. At the far side, Fotis led us over to the battlements, where the rock falls 700 feet sheer to the port. Palamedes was one of those legendary, unstormable citadels: having its own grazing within the walls, it could scarcely even be starved into surrender. And no wonder, we thought: one could not do so much as row a dinghy out to sea, or drive a cart in the Argolid, without a watcher in the fortress above Nauplion knowing of it at once.

We clambered down into one of the forts, the one called after Miltiades. Here, Fotis told us, the nineteenth-century patriot Kolokotronis was imprisoned, through the conspiracy of his jealous opponents, after having successfully led the partisans against the Turks during the Greek War of Independence. (The first Greek Government was established in Nauplion in 1829, at a time when Athens was little more than a village.) Near the ruins of St George's Chapel, where the caretaker's family were setting about their morning chores, had stood the guillotine – the instrument which, according to some cynics, was soon to become the symbol of patriotism and liberation. And certainly the infant nation began its career, here in Nauplion, with the same violent blood and bile that have embittered its history ever since: the first Prime Minister, Capodistria, was assassinated by members of a rival family at a spot 200 yards from our hotel, as he left the Church of St Spiridion.

By now the sky was brightening rapidly, and we climbed up again onto the battlements, leaving behind us a ready-made set for *Macbeth* – or rather one should say, remembering Kolokotronis, for *Fidelio*. We were just in time. As we looked across the rugged landscape that separated us from Epidauros and the Saronic Gulf, one of the most distant line of hills seemed to come alive, first turning itself into an intense shadow and then taking fire. For perhaps the millionth time since the words were first used, the Great God had appeared once more in his diurnal glory.

Down on the quayside after breakfast, gravity was in command again – almost. We were carrying out a quick film-test, using a polychrome collection of pottery bowls, jugs, flowerpots and household gadgets arranged in front of a local coasting-vessel. Alec pulled from his pocket a small jar, apparently a mustard-pot, and handed it to June for her to open. She obliged. With a

43

squawk, a long yellow jack-in-the-box leapt up out of the pot on its spring. (Collapse of all concerned. . . .)

★   ★   ★

Once again, our two parties began their journeys across the Peloponnese independently. Leaving the Volkswagen with its team behind in Nauplion to finish off their work, we set off ahead and visited Mycenae. Since March had only just begun, we had the site to ourselves. The anemones were in flower, their deep crimson heads scattered about the grass of the citadel like the blood of Agamemnon. Pausing from his dramatic recital of the crimes of Clytemnestra and Aegisthus (declaimed in the purest Greek), the guide clambered down the slope behind the Royal Palace – 'Orestes came along this path *here*, and in through the back door *there* . . .' – collecting handfuls of the blood-red anemones as he went, and, as we made our way back down to the car, he pressed them upon us with a gesture which was partly hospitable, partly deprecatory.

But it was not the old, well-known legends we were after, dramatic and evocative though they might be. From Agamemnon's fatal bathroom we had gazed West, across the laden orange-trees filling the plain of Argos, to the barrier of mountains behind, where Ziria, in its Alpine winter coat of snow, still dominated the spring landscape. We stopped to buy oranges from a stall by the roadside, and drove back into Argos, but this time we took the right-hand fork, and headed South along the road leading to Arcadia.

Among the Erewhons of the earth, Arcadia stands high. From the Garden of Eden through the Gardens of the Hesperides to the Islamic Paradise (for 'Paradise', the Persian *firdaus*, was originally another word for 'garden' – since to desert-dwellers a few shady trees, with flowers and grass around a spring, were paradise enough), from Atlantis through Bohemia and Illyria to the *Terra Incognita Australis* of the Pacific explorers, one Utopia after another has captured the human imagination, and has given poets and painters the opportunity for depicting their ideal of human existence. Thus, over the centuries, the name of Arcadia has come to stand for an ideal of life: a perfect type of withdrawn rural existence, exempt from the storms of politics and the tensions of city life. In the common mind of Western Europeans, the country folk of Arcadia pursue a life which never was, on sea or land, bathed in the perpetual evening glow borrowed by Claude and Poussin from their memories of the Roman Campagna. The climate of their imagined homeland is at the same time temperate, equable and certain; a quantum of honest toil is rewarded by ample fruitfulness without glut; love is always kind and requited; age brings dignity rather than querulousness; death comes gently and without pain. Sheltered miraculously from envy, misfortune and fall-out, the Arcadians need never let their minds wander beyond their own oak-shaded hills and lush water-meadows.

This 'Arcadia' of the European imagination exists, by now, at two removes from the original reality. The fictional Arcadia was first conceived in Rome, just as the city was becoming a great imperial power. During the second century B.C., Greece had been 'liberated' from the Macedonians and absorbed into the Roman world without upsetting the Republic's political digestion. By the last years of the old era, however, the frontiers of the Empire were expanding more rapidly than domestic politics could accommodate; and the politics of Rome were beginning to acquire that Latin-American tone (all conspiracies and *coups d'état*) which was later to become so characteristic. Shaken by the turmoil incidental to Rome's new power and prosperity, poets such as Virgil, Horace and Juvenal turned jaundiced eyes on their fellow-citizens, and dreamed up – essentially as a standard of criticism – an ideal of rustic felicity, free from the corruption, noise and uncertainty which they saw blossoming foetidly around them. Where did they get the idea from? Did it come from travellers' tales? Was it a result of cheerful letters, sent home by District Commissioners in the Roman Colonial Service? Was it the inaccessibility of the central Peloponnese that woke this enthusiasm? Or did some first-hand knowledge lead the Roman poets to locate their own Utopia in the region to which we were now going?

45

Certainly they all looked at the countryside through the eyes of townees. For then, as now, the realities of agriculture appeared in a different light to those who knew them at first hand, throughout their whole lives. The farm-labourers of Italy were already 'voting with their feet', tramping to Rome in the hope of finding a stimulus and opportunity missing from their bucolic paradise. In the eyes of Virgil and Horace, this rural depopulation was the result of a misunderstanding. Lying on a couch among his olive-trees, on the country estate presented to him by Maecenas, Horace was puzzled that anyone should prefer the city to the country. The eternal theme of urban-rural misunderstanding enters literature: how happy the farmers would be *sua si bona norint* – if only they counted their blessings, and recognized when they were well-off!

The Arcadian idyll germinated, grew, and flowered again at the time of the Renaissance. It had a double attraction. The sixteenth century had brought to Europe something of the expansion and turmoil known to the Rome of the early Caesars. But it brought also, in the form of the Humanist movement, an intellectual revival whose ambitions were focused on ideals borrowed from classical Greece. For the Humanists and their successors, Arcadia was a 'natural': over the next 300 years, the fictional Arcadia of Virgil and Horace became the starting-point for further flights of the imagination. The immediate question facing us was this: had the double idealization destroyed every single connection between the two Arcadias, of the literary imagination and of geographical reality?

The guide-book was unpromising: 'The presence of mountains exceeding 1,000 metres, covered by snow several times during the winter, brusquely chills the winds passing over them . . . notably in Arcadia.' Little more than five miles south of Argos, the road turned sharply inland and began to scramble doggedly up the mountains. The plain behind Argos had been rich and idyllic, but now we soon left the orange-groves behind. In great sweeping zig-zags the road climbed, first onto maquis-covered spurs with a last grand view back to Nauplion across the Mediterranean blue of the bay, then onto bare downland where the sparse trees showed no signs of breaking into leaf. There was one Utopian moment when, after crawling our way up through the deepest crevices of the hills to a height of nearly 3,000 feet, we at last broke out into the interior, to find ourselves at the edge of a rolling, sub-alpine plain which humped itself gently away and away to a distant rim of blue hills. (So, too, the hero of Erewhon finally breasted the mountains and, in a moment, found himself facing the mysterious land behind them.) The true, geographical Arcadia, as we soon saw, was no lush lowland paradise of alluvial plains and deep, rich earth, but rather an elevated plateau which, with its thin soil and exposed aspect, recalled the more rigorous parts of the French *Massif Central*. The farmers of antiquity could make a living hereabouts, certainly, and they would surely be left to themselves in the process; for the main arteries of the Ancient World were the sea-routes, and no-one would have climbed the natural battlements into Arcadia *en route* to anywhere else. Yet, however rustic and withdrawn, life here could never have been easy in any age.

This time we kept our appointment with Fotis and the van without difficulty, and by two o'clock we were sitting down to lunch in Tripolis. From there on, the map showed two roads over to Vytina: a lesser but more direct road that would take us through the forested hills and by way of Alonistaina, the mountain village where Fotis and Alec expected to find the terrain we were looking for, and a longer but better-made road around the foot of the hill. We set off in convoy along the minor road but got only a couple of miles. Then Alec, fearing to hear his precious cameras and equipment bumping around as the hard-sprung van bounced over the potholes, stopped and asked if we would mind taking the longer way round. We agreed, and turned back. The decision proved doubly wise, for, having reached the outskirts of Vytina and taken the back lane towards Alonistaina, we found our way blocked by another obstacle. Little more than two miles up the stony track into the fir-woods, the snow was lying in thick patches, and these soon gave way to an icy layer on which the blue van first crunched, then whirred, then slid, skidded and slipped.

47

Alec caught the van with the brake six inches from the edge, and we stopped too. Ahead of us, the snow-covered track curved away uphill into the dark forest: several miles of climbing evidently remained before we could hope for any improvement. Leaving aside immediate problems, there was one consolation: the Spring thaw had not gone as far as we had feared, and we should find snow easily accessible. For the moment, however, we had somehow to prevent the van from falling sideways into the trees, and having rescued it we must make our way back to Vytina for the night. The first task was delicate rather than dangerous. With its better traction, the car could be reversed without difficulty down past the snowline to a turning-point. The van took longer to extricate: with fir-branches under the wheels, much man-handling, and not too much power on the engine, we edged it inch by inch back past the danger-point. Since there was no way on by this road, we should have to reconnoitre an alternative method of reaching a point from which we could do our necessary filming. That could only be done at Vytina. With some relief, we drove gently back down the track, and came out of the trees within sight of the town. At that moment we had a first intimation that, after all, the gods might perhaps be on our side. For there, scattered along the roadside verge and across the meadow under the edge of the woods, there were dots of flame among the grass which caught my eye and brought me to a stop. *Krokoi!* It was now March, and I had given up hope of finding the wild orange crocus (about which Herakles and Betty had been so patronizing) still in flower; but here on its own ground, at a height of some 3,500 feet, it was still at its best – not the great stubby thumb of colour that gardeners know as the Dutch Yellow, but, instead, a little-finger of a flower, holding itself open towards the afternoon sun from the protective shelter of the rough tussocky grass.

Quail thrummed up from our feet as we tramped across the meadow back to the car, savouring the Horatian pleasures of being away from the great city. Vytina was no metropolis, merely a little Alpine town at a crossroads, linking the neighbouring farms to the commerce of the main road and providing a few beds for summer visitors. Halting us in the main square, Fotis whispered, 'Leave this to me', and marched into the only visible café-cum-hotel, loudly demanding to see the Mayor. The scene that followed could have taken place anywhere in the world, and at times, we felt as though we were hiring Sherpas in the Upper Himalayas. The tremors of the grapevine soon brought the Mayor onto the scene: a pleasant, round-faced man in a cloth cap and overcoat, with shallow blue eyes and the look of an un-ambitious grocer. Fotis (we realized) was flapping his left hand in our direction from behind his back, and we took this as a sign to join him. There were formal introductions all round and the mayor signalled to the lurking café-proprietor for cups of coffee. In no time our expedition acquired an unlooked-for im-portance. We were in the Peloponnese (well, strictly speaking, Fotis was . . .) to do some filming on behalf of the Minister of Blank; the Minister would be pleased to know that the Mayor and citizens of Vytina had been thoroughly co-operative, and had given all the help they could to these visitors to Greece – who were also, in a manner of speaking, *guests*. The Mayor inclined his head gravely, to indicate that all the modest facilities of Vytina were of course at our command. What were our needs? Some snow, some mules, some men? Those things should not be hard to arrange.

Hands were clapped, small boys were sent running, Fotis and the Mayor interviewed two or three of the local men who were standing around the café table, silent and curious, shifting their weight from boot to boot. Meanwhile we ordered supper, and the proprietor fixed us up with rooms for the night – white-washed cells with simple wire-sprung beds and small metal stoves which we soon had spitting, crackling and belching out acrid wood-smoke. Before long we were on terms of somewhat uncertain familiarity both with the Mayor and with the hotel-keeper, who turned out to be the local Conservative political organizer and had a somewhat superior habit of referring to the Minister of Blank as '*my* Minister'. (Fotis had got us bedrooms double-quick, by alleging that we were 'personal friends' of the Minister.) More important, we made the acquaintance of Christo, who was prepared to hire us mules the next day, and who swore in a very convincing tone that he knew of 'a fountain' where he had seen 'lots of snow' with his own eyes 'just the other day'. Yes, he said, it faced a little West of South, and the sun should be well onto it by about eleven o'clock in the morning; and we should be able to get up there with the mules without any difficulty. All right then, we said: 100 drachmas? Done! Make it eight o'clock next morning, so as to give us all plenty of time to load and get away.

*   *   *

The night was sparkling clear, and we woke to a crisp frost. We blew on our fingers, and decided that the smoke from the stoves would be the lesser of two evils: by flaring them up, we at least managed to heat an old coffee-tin full of water for a warm wash. Outside our window there was an explosion of sound, as the village square suddenly became a maelstrom of black goats; another explosion, as the goats were replaced by children on their way to school; then a leisurely clip-clop, as Christo led his three mules across to the corner by the hotel, and tethered them below a line of washing. It was a complicated business getting all the bulky boxes of film equipment conveniently stowed on the pack-saddles, but by half-past eight we were away, with Christo leading Marco, Billy-oh, and the third (nameless and much less characterful) mule at their own natural speed, and the rest of us walking cheerfully ahead. Fotis and his three companions were again in good form. The day was cool but sunny, and (we all agreed) a walk in the country was just the thing. Alec was in a good humour. At supper last night, he had put his 'mustard pot' on the table and had once again caught June out completely: on top of that, he had achieved a near-miss with an explosive cigar. Coulis flourished a small-bore pistol, with whose help he was confident of filling his knapsack with finches and similar ferocious game-birds. As for George: our company had evoked in him a brand-new personality of great eccentricity – a tall and spindly English country gentleman, with projecting front teeth, porkpie hat and sporting-cum-military umbrella. (This umbrella nevertheless betrayed a residual schizophrenia, jumping nervously from role to role. At times it was the military man's swagger-stick, at times his rifle, at other times again the landowner's switch or the point-to-pointer's shooting-stick.) Gazed at toler-antly by a few dawdling laggards of school-children, we strode out into the country.

A mile out of town a water-tank stood beside the road, and there we waited for the pack-train to catch us up. Christo watered the animals and adjusted their loads, while they stood blowing out their nostrils and shaking their heads, the blue good-luck beads on their harness gleaming in the sunshine. Another half-mile further on, we turned off the road onto a hill-track. Coulis was not having much luck with his gun ('The trouble is,' said Fotis, 'the birds are deaf'), so Alec insisted on having a go. At the third shot he brought down a finch, and tramped on contentedly, plucking it as he went. George's temporary personality was exclaiming mono-syllabically at the view: 'Oh I say!' – 'My word!' – and (in-appropriately enough) 'By George!' Soon we were above the crocus-line and into the edge of the forest. The track led us up the side of a steep valley, well above the stream, and we began to see the snow on the wooded ridge at the head of the valley some way above us. As the path got steeper, men and animals both slowed up. After half-an-hour of climbing, Christo paused be-side the boggy patch formed by a trackside spring. It was just about time (I thought) for another rest, before we embarked on the last lap up to his 'fountain'. But no: this *was* the 'fountain' – the 'lots of snow' he had seen there must have melted some time ago, and by now primroses and coltsfoot were well in flower.

Once again we had to improvise a change of plan. We threaded our way down through the trees, with the camera-boxes and tripods on the mules' backs brushing against the trunks of the firs. Having reached the stream in the valley bottom, we clambered up along it until we crossed the snow-line. There we spent three hours re-enacting the Transformations of Water – that ubi-quitous substance whose versatility so impressed the first of the Greek natural philosophers, Thales of Miletus. A rushing stream was leaping among the rocks at our feet. A few feet away, at the edge of the snow bank, drops of water were slowly forming and dripping down to the newly-exposed earth below. Already a few plants were converting the matter of these drops into the structure of the first spring flowers, while conifer seedlings were thrusting out their bright green new growth. Further away, beyond the bank, the sun was beating down directly onto the sheets of snow, and a light haze hung over the snow where the moisture was being converted directly from solid form into vapour. Meanwhile the mules, relieved of their heavy loads, were puffing clouds of moist breath into the cold air from their nostrils. Seeing for ourselves how many varied forms water could take, even in so small an area, we could no longer wonder at the fact that Thales should have thought it, not merely versatile, but infinitely mutable – or that, as late as the seventeenth century A.D., J. B. van Helmont and Robert Boyle should have shared the same view.

The task of recording all of this was a slow one, requiring care and discrimination but, beyond that, only a matter of time. As always in filming work, there were moments when, stopping to look at ourselves as spectators, we were compelled to laugh aloud. I preserve the memory of two scenes in particular. In the first, I am being instructed to collect together into the field-of-view, just below the melting snow-line, some flowers which had care-lessly and thoughtlessly been growing some distance apart: '*Il faut arranger la Nature un peu.*' In the other, Fotis has his eye glued to the camera, and is focusing the close-up lens on to a fir twig which George is delicately holding: meanwhile, Alec is drenching the twig with water from a child's watering can, Coulis is propping up an aluminium reflector so as to intensify the sun-light on the water-drops, Helen is using George's umbrella/ rifle/shooting-stick to shelter the camera from Alec's 'rain', and June is concentrating intently on her aesthetic task, explaining to Fotis in Basic English *exactly* what image she wants him to register.

By a quarter-to-two, it is all over. We trudge contentedly down the valley, thankful that the sun had stayed out, and that our polyglot team has worked together happily and – to all appearances – effectively. 'Did you hear about the two cats?' asks Fotis. 'One cat said to another "Miaow"; and the other replied "Cock-a-doodle-doo". "Why did you say that?" asked the first cat. "Oh," answered the second cat proudly, "*I* speak foreign languages!".' Now that we are on our way back downhill, we take it in turns to ride on the mules, perching uncomfortably on top of the sharp-cornered boxes and spiky tripods. While Helen rides beside the stream, June and Fotis clamber up towards the hill path, reminiscing about June's previous visit to Greece, when the two of them had spent several weeks filming together at Samos and Athens. June recalls how, one evening, they had been exchanging songs and jokes, when Fotis and Herakles had solemnly told her 'their favourite English joke'. 'There are two fishes, in middle of ocean. One fish, he says to other fish, "What is that big black shadow over us?" "Not to worry," say other fish, "that is nothing, that is only Queen Elizabeth's bottom".' George and I follow along behind, taking snapshots of the scenery, and I find that the imitation Englishman has almost deserted him: left alone with his camera and some beautiful subjects, he is as near an undivided person as he can be. Further down the hill, I try taking a ride on one of the mules myself, but it is an uncomfortable business: the track is rocky and uneven, the bulky equipment rolls around on the saddle, and the wretched animal is suffering from wind. (Fotis comes up to us at a critical moment, and remarks, 'Your mule is a Jet, I see.')

We for our own part were well satisfied. By itself, the morning's work justified the trip into the Peloponnese, and we planned after lunch to set off on the first stage of our journey, on to Delphi (where we were to reconnoitre for a later visit), and so back to Athens. Fotis and his three colleagues still had two or three days' work to do for the Ministry, and would stay behind in Arcadia. The parting was affectionate, and unexpectedly protracted. When we finally got back to Vytina, the boys settled down for a late lunch in a back street *taverna*, and Alec, whipping out a cigarette tin from his pocket, produced the plucked body of the finch he had shot: this went on to the charcoal grill, along with the rest of our lunch. To our English embarrassment, June

53

and I found ourselves expected to eat it, and we did so with simulated appreciation – for in Greece, as in Arabia, such a morsel must never be refused, however unaccustomed or distasteful. Finally, we managed to get the car loaded up again, and drove off westwards to a chorus of reciprocal regrets.

The parting was only temporary. From then on, we were playing leap-frog most of the afternoon. A few miles out of town, we stopped the car to fill our water-bottles from a convenient stream, and we were just about to go on again when the little blue van bundled up noisily, heads bristling out of all windows. We set off once more, hoping to reach Olympia by evening: the road climbed again, and crossed a desolate stretch of sandy humps, recalling the most barren parts of Nevada. Soon afterwards, it became evident that we had crossed the far rim of the central plateau, and were beginning to drop down towards the Alpheus. In the grass beside the road, some small purple iris were already in flower, and we stopped to inspect them: with a rattle, a toot and a cheer, the Volkswagen raced past us, waving hands sprouting from it. A mile or so further on we turned a corner, and there they were again, pulled into a lay-by at the edge of the precipitous road. From this point, one looked clear across a side-valley at the extraordinary town of Langadhia. We stopped too. A town of 3,000 people, devoid of any visible means of livelihood, was spread vertically up the face of a sterile hillside. Shaking hands for 'really the last time', we coasted off down the hill, leaving the quartet behind to their own Arcadian devices. Beyond Langadhia – a town which, as we discovered later, supports itself on stonemasonry – the road spilled sharply down a gorge towards the lowlands. Ears popping, we followed it down, half-regretting the enclosed, protected mountain-land we were leaving behind us. After all, Arcadia might not be lush and generous, yet it was certainly peaceful, and the ring of mountains shutting it off from the outer world still helped to defend it against external pressures and anxieties.

Half-an-hour later, we were back in a land of oranges and lemons: we had dropped from 4,000 feet to 400. Less than one more hour, and we were running through tobacco fields along the fertile valley of the Alpheus. The tourist hotel at Olympia was grand and clean. After Vytina, the beds were all the softer, and just for one night we were content to exchange our smoky wood stove for central-heating radiators. Having bathed and changed into our least untidy clothes, we ordered drinks and settled down in the main lounge. By now, it was nearly eight o'clock, and we should soon have to brace ourselves for a hotel dinner. The room was furnished cheerfully enough, but it was filled with the Trappist hush that is generated whenever three or four Anglo-Saxons are gathered together in a public sitting-room – a silence broken only by the grunting of two Mid-Western bores, who were exchanging rival monologues in one corner. Beside the fireplace the tour-leader (for this was a coach-party from Athens) stretched her legs wearily towards the glow, and let the strain run out of her eyes and limbs. We were pulling ourselves together for the coming ordeal, when there was a tramping on the stairs. Four familiar faces appeared round the corner: 'Ah, we have found you.' Against the background of trimly-tailored and primly-dressed tourists, they looked wonderfully out-of-place: as though Pan and three fauns had wandered into the hotel from the surrounding woods. They pulled us up out of our chairs, and propelled us down the imposing stairway, exclaiming cheerfully in loud voices: 'We cannot live without "the Nuffield"!'

We walked down the middle of the village street arm-in-arm, blind to the picture-postcard stalls and souvenir shops. At the far end, beyond the road junction, there was the customary *taverna*. In one, but only one respect, the tourist-trade had left its mark – there were tablecloths. We sat down and clapped our hands. By now we could all recite, or sing, the inevitable menu:

Tarama	Dolmades	Fasoulia	
Paidakia	Souvlakia	Kokoretsi	
Psari	Psomi	Krasi	Nero

We made our choice. The owner brought out two flasks of wine, one of *retsina* and another – for the weaker English – unresinated. His wife put down her knitting for a moment, to help lay our places: the cooking, of course, would be his job. Alec felt in his pocket for his mustard-pot, glanced round the table, and thought better of it. A benign look came over Fotis's face and he launched into one of his stories – was it about two birds. . . . ? Coulis sat back, tipping his chair and sipping *retsina*, as he smiled quietly to himself. I glanced at George, whose face was a playground of rival personalities, and wondered who he was going to be tonight. We were at home.

★   ★   ★

At the hotel, our bedroom was at the very end of the wing. The glass wall slid back on runners, and I stepped out on to the balcony. It was early morning. A rough track led up to the right beyond the hotel, round the brow of a fir-covered hill. To the left the grassy slope fell away, and a pair of umbrella-pines framed a distant view, across the water-meadows of the Alpheus to the wooded hills beyond. The first sunlight was filtering down the valley, drawing up a gentle haze from the river. Almost alone in all Greece, the valley of Olympia looked lush and fertile, with the generosity of our dreamland Arcadia. This was a land for fauns all right; with reeds along the river, where the musical fancy of man (half human, half divine) could make pipes to charm both Nature and himself.

It was a moment for reflection. At dawn a man need not fight: he has time to wake and flex himself for the day. And here by the Alpheus one could feel especially *in with* Nature, even content to be *a part of* Nature. In their science and philosophy, as much as in their public mythology, the Greeks of the high classical period never saw man in any other way: they had no conception of that 'respectability' which involves renouncing our share of Nature, and standing apart from the world of natural drives and aspirations. Respectability has killed the demi-gods – Pan and the fauns along with the rest. Yet in a few places they have left their indelible mark; and here at Olympia, in a landscape worthy of Claude and Poussin, one can still feel a sense of their presence . . . just around the corner.

Yet we were, in fact, no longer in Arcadia: we had left it behind us the previous afternoon, when we reached the foot of the hills. This was Elis; and if Poussin had ever visited Greece, he need have gone no further, for he would have found all he wanted here, without troubling to scale the rugged hills into the real Arcadia. After breakfast we should be setting off, on our way through Patras to Itea and Delphi: first North, and later East. Fotis and his colleagues were up and away before us, and by the time we left they were already pulling their way up the hillside that Poussin never dared. As we drove down the village street in our Citroen, the little blue Volkswagen van had disappeared. The fauns had fled away.

4 · The Waters of Parnassus

In and out, in and out, through the same tissues: the human body reacts by building a defensive layer of scar-tissue around the path of the hypodermic needle. In this layer, normal bodily processes are suspended or distorted, the body's reactions to this localized invasion dominating everything else. From the organism's point of view, the needle – with everything around it – remains something essentially alien, part of the external world, a 'foreign body'.

Tourism affects a country in the same way – like a series of repeated injections. And it would be no good (I thought, as the tourist-coach from Olympia lumbered after us onto the ferry at Aiyion) confining our view of the Greek countryside and country life to the regions of 'scar-tissue' around the established tourist-routes. We needed something more than a 'tourist's-eye view'; and the plain fact could not be ignored: these diesel-engined hypodermics, discharging their foreign bodies at the great classical sites day after day, were evoking the unavoidable organic response – grand hotels, mass-produced souvenirs, local inflation, touts – all the amenities of the cosmopolitan travel-industry. Evidently the normal processes of Greek life could scarcely hope to survive the invasion: least of all, that unquestioning pride in pouring out for the visitor, without stint and (of course) without charge, all the available resources of one's hospitality.

As things turned out, we had no real cause to worry. We ourselves were not bound for Delphi itself, but for the village of Chrysso, which lies half-way up the hillside, as you climb from the olive-groves towards the spur of Parnassus which hides the sacred shrine. The mile separating the two places was enough. In Delphi itself, the layers of 'scar-tissue' are pretty thick. Not surprisingly, the people of Delphi know very well where the butter on their bread comes from. In the eighteen-nineties, at the time of the great archaeological excavations, the inhabitants were compelled to leave their homes, the whole village being moved bodily a quarter of a mile, away from the site of the shrine; and their lives are still geared closely to the recurrent invasions of 'foreign bodies'. Nor is this commercialism anything new at Delphi. The pains, profits and perils of the tourist industry are not a feature of the twentieth century alone: in places such as this, they are an old, old story. Indeed, the twentieth-century rediscovery of Delphi's tourist attractions still has some way to go before it can recapture all the full-blooded vulgarity and vitality of its earlier flowerings. The temples surrounding the ancient oracle were not tucked away in a rural retreat, far from the intruding gaze of common men. Anything but – they formed the Mecca of antiquity, and men came to them in their thousands from all over the Greek world. The great festivals were busy, rowdy and – without doubt – commercialized. Where the coach-parties now tread decorously along the trimly-kept paths of the Sacred Way, there pressed crowds of suppliants, delegates and hangers-on, with money in their pockets and time on their hands; the theatre itself, that great semi-circular arena capable of seating 5,000 people at a time, should remind us what Delphi was like at its prime; and further up the hill again, where the path from the Castalian spring reaches the foot of the towering cliffs, a silent belt of pine trees now surrounds . . . nothing less than a full-scale race-track, with seats for 20,000, and standing room for many more.

Yet the effects are localized. One does not have to go very far to get back into the authentic life of the Greek countryside. In its early days Chrysso, too, was swept into the maelstrom of Delphic commerce. For a time, indeed, the inhabitants of Chrysso had a very profitable stranglehold on the tourist trade. Then as now, Itea played Jeddah to Delphi's Mecca, and the flood of pilgrims coming to Delphi by sea was funnelled up the narrow valley which climbs from the port to the shrine. By its position, Chrysso controlled this valley absolutely, and the men of Chrysso took full advantage of the fact. They filled their pockets to such effect that the rapacities of Delphi itself were overshadowed. By 600 B.C. the guardians of the shrine had had enough: allying themselves with their most powerful patrons and customers, they declared war on Chrysso, and within ten years they had broken its stranglehold for good. Now, in the twentieth century, it is a small country town, up whose main street the diesel coaches daily pound their way, zig-zagging to and fro across the hillside as they gain height for the last crest which leads to Delphi.

Once again, June's earlier filming-trip to Greece gave us a flying start. Through Fotis and his friends, we had been drawn into the life of Athens from the moment of our arrival: now, thanks to Barbara and her family, we were to have the same experience outside the city. Visiting Chrysso three times in as many months, we were able to break through, past the scar-tissue and the formal demands of *philoxenia*, to the daily life behind them. Inevitably, however, our first visit was consecrated to formalities. June came to the place as an old friend, as a stranger, as a stranger returning from far away, returning after more than two years, returning with a husband. . . . Every aspect of the situation created a further claim, and pitched the demands of hospitality the higher. There could be no question of escaping the fullest rigours of a Greek welcome.

*   *   *

The converted landing-craft rounded the little island which sits in the middle of the bay like a traffic roundabout – a low grass-covered dome of rock, naked of any building except for the minute white chapel at its topmost point. Beyond it, the full length of the Itea waterfront came into view. Two coastal cargo-boats were tied up at the single jetty, and the quay beyond was backed by a row of low white buildings, many of them (apparently) in course of repair. Contrasted with the vast natural amphitheatre behind it, the little town looked dusty and un-impressive; for, as we drifted the last 100 yards towards the landing-stage, the whole view was dominated, not by the works of man, but by the long Southern flank of Parnassus, which here stares down across the coastal plain. On either hand, mountain ridges press out to sea, delimiting plain and bay between a giant finger and thumb. Inland, over and between the houses of the town, we could just see the first green of the olive-groves of Amphissa, which fill the whole amphitheatre below Parnassus and are irrigated by its melted snows.

Whatever the time of day or night, and however unimportant it may be, the arrival of any boat provides Greeks with an excuse for a crowd. As we stepped ashore, two men detached themselves from the mêlée: our reception had begun. One of them June recognized at once as Elias, Barbara's uncle by marriage. He was the taller and older of the two, with dark hair and sharply-cut features – like a younger and more heavily jowled Bertrand Russell. He came foward with a half-hesitation, the warmth in his eyes fighting against a natural reserve. His younger companion was a complete contrast: fairer, shorter, more effusive, with pink cheeks snapping from time to time into an automatic grin, and prominent gold fillings in his molars. Elias had time only to murmur introductions ('My cousin Louis . . .') before the flood of volubility began:

'Kindly walk this way. Let us drink something. I am making new café' (his hand waved towards the building-workers), 'new restaurant, new dancing. You must come eat, drink, dance. . . . Itea changing' (another wave of the hand at the clouds of cement, which were drifting in the air along the quay). 'Very comfortable ship, very comfortable tourist-coach, very comfortable yacht. . . .'

June and the others let themselves be shepherded along the jetty, while I turned back to the ferry. By the time I had driven the car ashore and parked it, they were all seated at tables outside the bar. I came up to find Cousin Louis still in spate:

' . . . I ships' chandler. I know English yachtsman, English yachtsman know me. English lorths, English lathies come Itea on yacht. Lorth X – – –, Lorth Y – – –, they all come see me. . . .'

Elias staunched the flow for long enough to send Louis for the drinks, and June could at last begin on all her inquiries. Yes, his wife Evthemia was well; and his small daughter; and Barbara herself; and the olive-crop was very promising; and Mrs Bessy, who was sorry to have missed June on her previous visit two years ago, was expecting us – all of this coming across in his slow quiet Greek.

After our regulation drink, we left Cousin Louis to continue prowling the quay, dropped Elias at his olive-packing factory, and set off inland for Chrysso: two miles under the olive trees, turn right where the roads from Athens and Amphissa meet, then sharply uphill in long raking traverses to where the little town lies astride the road. We passed right through the central *plateia*, with its triangle of flagstones shadowed by plane-trees, and the steep stairway climbing up behind the communal fountain – a row of spouts in a stone wall, out of which fresh Parnassus spring-water gushes into large basins the whole year round. The road climbed another quarter of a mile, until it was right outside the village, hairpinned sharply to the left past the cemetery, and wound through the houses again at a higher level. At the point where the steps from the fountain met the road once more, there was a smaller, upper *plateia*: a small patch of tree-shaded gravel, fronted by a parapet from which the view extended right across Itea and the gulf beyond, to the snow-capped mountains of the Peloponnese. Mrs Bessy's house was a short way down the steps.

We were immediately engulfed in affection and hospitality, though these two different receptions alternated disconcertingly, since their respective demands in part conflicted. Evthemia is as short as June and younger, though with her dark clothes and lined country face she looked older. In her initial excitement, she kissed her lovingly on both cheeks, but soon fell back into formality, and for the whole of our first visit she kept switching in the same way between unthinking merriment and her formal obligations as our hostess. Mrs Bessy came foward to be intro-duced: older, paler, better cared-for, a woman with at least half a foot outside her village, yet still dressed in the deepest widow's weeds, from the black bandeau on her hair to her black stockings and shoes. (As Elias later explained, her husband had died only two years and seven months back; until the three years of deepest

mourning were over it would scarcely be decent for her to relax –
for instance, by listening to the wireless.) They showed us round
the back of the main house into the outbuilding where, as we
soon discovered, three-quarters of their lives were lived. A plain
wooden table filled the centre of the room, the kitchen range and
sink stood against two of the walls, cupboards and beds against
the other two. The ceiling was low, and a single window looked
out on the yard and the hen-run. Taking June by both hands,
Evthemia drew her inside, smiling, gesturing and chattering in
Greek as she bustled around. Mrs Bessy was beginning on a conversation in halting, schoolbook English, when the latch on the
door lifted and a young girl came in. She was firmly built, with a
square face, and straight dark hair drawn back into two clips:
rather ordinary features were offset by brown eyes full of deep
intelligence. She looked shyly round the room to June, then came
forward to embrace her with the same mixture of gravity and
warmth that had been so marked in Elias earlier. This was
Evthemia's niece, and June's special favourite, Barbara.

The three women now set about their duties in earnest, and we
too in return had our own obligations to fulfil. The celebration
started in a small way, miniature liqueur glasses filled with the
sweet local cordial called, a little inappropriately, *koniak*. With
this, there came the round, crumbly *beignets*, drenched in a fine
white sugar, which are the traditional greeting-cakes of the
Greek countryside. Then the kettle was put on, in honour of the
English, and we drank tea with lemon and mountains of sugar,
while from the main house Barbara and Evthemia fetched a
veritable mountain-range of cakes and buns and sweetmeats and
biscuits and jams and *petit-fours* and I don't know what; so that,
by the time Elias arrived home from work, we were in a mood to
cry 'Pax!' But things were only beginning. 'Now,' announced
Mrs Bessy, 'Mr Elias wish . . . show you . . . Chrysso . . . while
we' – we listened incredulously – 'make ready . . . supper.'

Evidently our own performance, as guests, was going to compare unfavourably with their performance as hosts, so we prepared ourselves for as brisk and energetic a conducted tour of the
town as could be packed into half-an-hour. Elias led the way, and

Barbara followed, holding June by the hand in a touching mixture of diffidence and demonstrativeness. We encouraged Elias to take us wherever he would, uphill and downhill, to the olive factory, to the three churches, to the lower *plateia*, down the road to the open country, up the steps again to see the view . . . anything to shake down the first over-ample meal, and prepare us for the further ordeal of hospitality to come.

Back to our duties. Tea had been a mere snack. Serious gastronomic business was prefaced by plates of *bourekakia* – savoury mouthfuls of spinach, or meat, or mushroom, or what-you-please, baked in little triangular pockets of *börek* (Turkish *millefeuille* pastry). Evthemia and Mrs Bessie carried them round the room, popping them into our mouths with their own fingers, and coaxing us after only a moment's rest to accept more. We soon felt like baby birds, our unwilling beaks confronted with an endless supply of worms. But this too was only the *hors d'oeuvre*. Properly speaking, the meal began only when we graduated to man-sized plates of lamb, served together with glasses of retsina and half-a-dozen dishes full of substantial vegetables. Duty compelled us to accept some at least of all these, and two in particular stuck in our memories – and our throats. One we had met before. It was a kind of wild spinach generally referred to as *khorta tou vounou* (or 'herbs off the mountain'), and was regarded as a great delicacy: we had done our best to like it, but still found it unpalatable, even though not inedible. The other was unique in our experience – dozens of pale spheres floating in a brown watery liquid, whiter and rounder than the pickled onions of an English pub, gleaming with the malevolence of sheep's-eyes. I still do not know what exactly they were. Bessie called them 'bulbs'. Perhaps they *were* crocus bulbs, though I had always understood that they were mildly poisonous. These at any rate had a blank, neutral taste, and so slithered around the tongue that they were more easily swallowed whole than trapped between the teeth and bitten. Evthemia spooned them liberally on to our plates, and watched to see how we enjoyed them. She was determined to set our hesitations at rest. '*Kalo ya to stomacha*,' she declared, in a soothing tone; and this phrase –

(a) *above* Tasso, the strong man
(b) *below* Hobby-horse riders

I. CARNIVAL AT ATHENS

(a) *above* Callas *en tenue de* 'gentleman'
(b) *below* Necessity is the mother . . .

2. VYTINA

(a) *above* Efthemia
(b) *below* Harvesting olives

3. CHRYSSO

4. THE HARBOUR AT AEGINA

5. THE POTTER OF SIFNOS

(a) *above Jack London* in a cove near the crater
(b) *below* Making the Easter cakes

6. SANTORINI

7. THE TOWN OF SANTORINI

(a) *above* The harbour and zigzag track up to the town
(b) *below* Spice-seller

8. SANTORINI

'good for the digestion' – was one we heard much more of before we left Chrysso.

The meal was not finished. Bessie and Evthemia had spent three days making the cakes: now it was up to us to do our part. Replenished from an inexhaustible store, the mountainous plates of buns and cake-squares and beignets and sweetmeats reappeared, piled even higher than before; and we set out on this further lap with faint hearts and glazed eyes. More tea, another round of cognac to top off the retsina and then, just as we were about to lapse into unconsciousness, a bowl full of oranges. Throughout the whole proceedings, between every mouthful, interpreting each phrase of the conversation and adding half-a-dozen of her own, Mrs Bessie's schoolbook English rang around the table and across the piles of plates, until we finally had to cry halt and admit surrender. Then and only then, when the first reciprocal duties of hospitality had been discharged, could we be permitted to go to sleep. We staggered in a daze up the staircase of the main house, and fell stupidly on to our beds.

*　　*　　*

We woke to find ourselves in the Germany of 1912. Bessie's husband had spent much of his career in the United States before returning to his native village, to plough his savings into 600 olive-trees and ostentatious furnishings for the domestic nest. The contents of the main reception-rooms seemed to have been lifted from the Wiesbaden of before the First World War: heavy chairs in black wood and red plush, solid sideboards with glass tops and lace runners, thick velvet curtaining. These rooms were – need one say? – never actually *used*. Even the copper geyser in the bathroom was inoperative and had probably never been connected: we washed in the basin, using water poured out of buckets. Life of any kind began only when one left this museum for the lower floor, and real, everyday life began only out-of-doors, in the outhouse. To have been permitted to enter those first-floor rooms at all was (we guessed) an uncommon privilege.

On our second day the gastronomic offensive continued with

little slackening. Breakfast was a repetition of tea, and at/midday Bessie took us to lunch in the tourist-hotel at Delphi, leaving Evthemia behind to re-group her forces for the evening assault. We had spent much of the morning climbing around the ruins of the shrine, yet even so felt hardly ready for more than a cup of *consommé* – 'Very well, then,' I heard June saying faintly, 'Just the very smallest omelette.' So we were delighted to hear that there was to be an afternoon expedition to a local beauty-spot, the Monastery of Prophetes Elias – the Prophet Elijah. This stands on a spur of Parnassus looking down on to the plain of Amphissa from a small plateau several hundred feet higher even than Delphi. Elias came back early from work in order to supervise the excursion. The road was too rough for our car, they declared, and the village taxi was activated for the occasion. This was a veteran Hispano-Suiza with an imposing brass radiator, which without difficulty swallowed into its cavernous interior a party of eight people besides the driver. *Philotimia* (I realized) would in any case have forbidden them to make the journey in their guests' own car; so we submitted, and bounced our way resignedly up the red dirt road to the monastery.

We were immediately glad we had come. Though the Church and its surrounding buildings were nothing out-of-the-ordinary, the view was superb. Immediately behind us the wall of Parnassus stretched away to the East in a continuous line, to meet the line of coastal hills coming up from the Gulf at the pass of Arachova. To the West, a similar range of hills swept upwards uninterruptedly, to culminate in the sharp and snowy peak of Giona. And below us, all the way from the sea-coast at Itea as far inland as Amphissa, there was spread out an unbroken sea of olive-groves, and this lapped the rocks at the foot of the very spur on which we stood. 'There,' exclaimed Elias, pointing out across the bay to a group of white houses which was just visible in the crook of the next headland, 'there is Galaxidhi, the port where *O Lorthos Veeron* landed in Greece.' We looked blank. '*O Lorthos Veeron*,' he repeated, as though we were being rather stupid, 'the poet'; and I grasped at last his reference to every Greek's favourite Englishman – Lord Byron. We smiled and nodded modestly, trying to accept the implied compliment on behalf of England without taking any personal credit to ourselves. Then, in a glow of Anglo-Hellenic friendship, we turned to meet the only remaining inhabitants of the little community – two old shepherds and the custodian.

By coming to Chrysso we had taken one step away from the modernities of Athens; but so far we had got back only to – say – the year 1910. There was still something early-twentieth-century about Bessie's tastes and aspirations which gave a definite period flavour to the whole household. (Evthemia, it should be explained, had been adopted in childhood by Bessie, who was herself childless; while Elias, Evthemia's husband, had succeeded to some of the formal prerogatives of Bessie's late spouse – though in most respects she herself remained the matriarch.) Up in the monastery, however, life was medieval. With ramshorn crooks and sheepskins sewn together into cloaks, their faces bronzed and beaten into a supple leather, the shepherds looked exactly as they would have done under the Turkish occupation – if not even in classical times. To mark our visit in the traditional way, the custodian sat us down on his whitewashed balcony and brought us each the ritual mouthful, a spoon of vanilla standing in a glass of cold water – what we later learned to call a 'submarine'.

After twenty minutes or so, Elias showed signs of wanting to collect us up; but at this point a spirit of rebellion entered into us. We had asked in the first place whether we might not make the expedition up to the monastery on foot, but this (for reasons of *philotimia*?) had been vetoed. Now June, who had not yet had a moment out of range of Mrs Bessie's monologue, and was anxious to get back onto her old terms with young Barbara, invited her to walk back down with us. But this too, it appeared, offended against some unwritten obligation. Elias bundled Barbara into the car, and we found ourselves setting off over the hillside with – of all people – Bessie herself as guide and companion. Irritation spurred our legs. Years of experience on Cader Idris and Great Gable made us sure-footed over the bracken-covered rocks, and once over the brow of the hill we

67

fairly bounced down the slope, rejoining the road 250 feet below. Bessie, in high heels, competed bravely with the unaccountable English, but in vain; so Helen, who felt that something should be done to keep her in countenance, lagged behind and took the full force of the monologue herself. But by now June and I had daemons in our legs, and by the time the antiquated Hispano-Suiza clattered past us on its return journey, we were a full 100 yards ahead of the other two. We stepped aside onto the verge, smiling encouragingly and ducking out of the way of the main cloud of dust. Half-an-hour later, we were at the outskirts of the town, and strode down the Delphi road to the upper *plateia* with blood at last flowing again through our veins. Was there something slightly dishonourable about our conduct? – perhaps so. But at times one can justifiably take advantage of the English reputation for eccentricity; and how else could we have prepared ourselves to face the next lap of the hospitality-marathon?

*   *   *

When we first visited Chrysso the trees were still bare, apart from the first almond-blossom. When we returned, the almonds were already forming, and the leaf-buds on the plane-trees were beginning to burst. This time we succeeded in passing beyond mere formalities to a deeper level. It was as well that we did, for we had work to do. At once, we were made aware how completely the life and aspirations of Chrysso and its people are rooted in the olive-trees that cover the plain of Amphissa – most of all in the black, glossy fruits that hang upon them. (The olives of Kalamata are those most reputed for the quality of their oil, but the Amphissa olives, swollen by the water of Parnassus, are known as the best eating-olives in Greece: the fattest of all sell in the corner-stores of New York City under the name of 'Jumbo Greek Olives'.) Not only is the town's whole economy based on the proceeds of the olive trade, but its annual cycle of life mirrors, too, the sequence of operations in the orchards. Now the picking season was almost over, and only the very end of the crop still had to be brought in: already the elders of the village, sitting around the main *plateia* in the dusk of evening, were talking over the prospects of the new year's crop.

Fotis and I reached the foot of the steps with Elias, turned into the square past the fountain, and sat down with them. Several of their faces were familiar to me from our earlier visit. There was the silent, prosperous-looking man of rising sixty, whose head and face were themselves shapely and well-nourished like a ripe olive: he sat slightly apart from the rest, in his trilby hat and Athenian overcoat, meditating (we guessed) on the fortunes of his own 1,000 trees. Elias introduced him to us as 'my partner'. Another man, in his early fifties, was 'a client': he was an equable man, with wavy hair going grey and a ready smile, and was wearing a rough, double-breasted blue suit which he left open in front – 'Ah, *Kyrios Stephanos*, so you're back! Sit down here. What will you have? Coffee? *Ouzo*? . . .' Elias, remembering his position as our host, waved the offer aside and ordered our drinks himself, while Fotis gradually led the conversation round to our own problems. As we talked, we were joined by another, much younger man. Tall, with broad shoulders and dark hair, he had the build of a man used to hard work, but with an unexpectedly fleshy look to his face and hands. Elias motioned to him to sit down quietly, and flicked with his fingers for another coffee to the café-owner across the street, though without missing a word of our conversation. Comna, the younger man, listened attentively, but in the presence of three of the village elders he put in hardly a word himself. Before long, they had come to the conclusion (Fotis explained) that only one man in the town still had a substantial number of olives to pick in, and Comna was sent off to bring him into the conference. A few minutes later Fotis had finished bargaining, and had arranged for a group of pickers to be assembled, whom we could film at work – weather permitting – around midday next day.

By the end of the next three days, we had seen for ourselves just about everything there was to be seen to do with olives and their handling. We saw the young sapling trees, green and supple, with the girth of – say – a pencil; young trees just coming into leaf; full-fruiting trees with trunks still sturdy and well-formed;

69

mature trees already contorted, but bearing more heavily than ever; and finally a few veterans, twenty-five feet high or more, their trunks sprawling in tormented shapes, with the new year's fresh growth still cascading, green and fruitful, from their crests. (There was no necessity, Elias assured us, for an olive *ever* to cease bearing, and many of the Amphissa trees were certainly hundreds of years old: yes indeed, Fotis confirmed, and there are still olive-trees in the plain of Athens which were already bearing fruit in Socrates' lifetime!) We turned off the road to Itea and drove along a rough track into the heart of the olive-groves. Low banks served to keep the irrigation-water enclosed around the feet of the trees. Along the edge of the irrigation-ditches anemones were in flower, in many shades of red and blue and purple and white. Away from the track to the left, we could hear the sound of smacking and thrashing, and the whipping whistle of long bamboos: the pickers were at work. We unloaded our equipment and humped it to the orchard, where the men were beating the trees with long sticks, while the girls stumped around on their haunches like Cossacks, and collected the fallen fruit into their aprons.

We visited next Elias' warehouse down in Itea, where the graded olives pass a six months' purgatory, steeping in enormous vats of brine to leach out the bitter juices of the raw fruit. (June winced, recalling how she had once accepted the gift of an olive straight off the tree from a poker-faced friend in California.) We visited also the olive-oil factory in Chrysso itself, where the fruit is first ground into pulp, which is shovelled into sacks; and the hissing steam-press next closes its cast-iron jaws onto a dozen sackfuls of pulp, piled one above the other, so that a cloudy golden stream of crude olive-oil exudes through the rough cloth sacking and runs down into a tank below. This piece of late nineteenth-century machinery somewhat disappointed us: 'All Done by Steam' – but perhaps that was inevitable. Yet somewhere in the neighbourhood, we asked Elias, might there not be some more ancient hand-powered press? If we were trying to convey the *feel* of an earlier age, linked even more closely to the fortunes of the sheep and the olive, this churning steam monster would look a bit of an anachronism. Elias consulted his colleagues in the factory – the manager and 'my client'. After a moment, light dawned on their faces: Yes, we could find what we wanted in a remote, hill-top village some ten miles away. Up there, they believed, the people were still using an entirely unmechanized press, of the kind we were interested in locating. It was up to us, of course, whether we thought it worth the trouble of making the journey. They themselves were clearly sceptical.

Next morning, however, found us driving along the back streets of Itea, aiming directly for the mountainside above which (they told us) we should find the village of Desfina. At the very foot of the precipice the road turned towards the sea, and ran as far as it could go without tipping into the waves; then it turned abruptly and clambered its way up the first fifty feet of the hill, shot round again and for 200 yards aimed straight out to sea; hairpinned inwards once more to a cleft in the rocks, out to another vertiginous drop, in to the beginnings of a steep mountain valley, out . . . in . . . out . . . in . . . till we were several hundred feet up above the curve of the bay. Though alarming, the road was passable, and showed more signs of maintenance than its extremely rough surface would have led one to expect – but then, we were told, the villagers of Desfina had built it by their own sweat and toil, at a time when the Government had refused to pay for it out of the taxes. A thousand feet up, the road stopped threatening to do a high-dive into the bay, and began to climb up the narrow valley towards a col – though, for all that we could see, there was going to be an equally steep drop beyond this. Now that we were away from the first vertiginous zig-zag, Helen and June breathed more freely, but our Greek companions went on unconcernedly singing a catchy little Hadzidakis tune in five/ eight time until we reached the brow of the hill. We came out abruptly into a quite unsuspected world: a green elevated saucer of land, some four or five miles across, closed in entirely by a stony rim of hill-tops, but providing by itself a living (of a kind) for several dozen farmers and their families. The road flattened out and dropped gently down into this fertile saucer. Beyond the northern rim, we could just see the wall of Parnassus – though it was hard to believe how deep a gorge separated this isolated world from the main massif beyond. We came round a low hill, and there on the far slope of the saucer stood a complete town of much the same size as Chrysso, securely grouped round a central spring and embodying centuries of history.

Overnight the weather had broken, and a heavy rainstorm at 5 a.m. had left the sky full of haze and clouds. In making our reconnaissance we had little hope of exploiting its results immediately; and, in the event, there was little we could have done. The olive-mill was there, all right, and after the usual formalities with the Mayor, and cups of coffee in the local bar, we were taken to see it. At the far end of a shed, a vertical axle from floor to ceiling carried a long horizontal pole: a horse was harnessed to this, and marched round and round, driving two heavy stone rollers over the mulch of olives. As at Chrysso, the crushed mass of skin, flesh and stones was shovelled into rough sacks, and put into a wooden press – itself built from olive-wood – which was driven from above by a capstan mechanism. The whole mechanism stood under a low, corrugated-iron roof, in the most impenetrably dark, broken-down stone barn that we could remember.

Strangers are strangers. When we arrived, three-quarters of the town's male population turned out to see what we were after, and most of these were now compressed into the shed. The crowd overflowed on to the rough flagged street outside, so that even through the main door little light penetrated into the building. Fotis asked a question, and half-a-dozen men jumped forward, applying themselves to the handles of the capstan. They leant on them rhythmically, singing as they set the capstan turning, but broke off from time to time laughing and chaffing one another, not caring to appear too serious about the job. For the finger of modernity had set its print even on Desfina, so that (as Fotis said) 'They know very well that it is out-of-date, and do not know whether to be proud or ashamed of it.'

Either way – to our regret – the thing was for the present unfilmable. Nothing but a vast battery of powerful lights could have pierced the black cavern of the barn in which the press stood. So we continued our reconnaissance elsewhere, holding our breath as the car crept down the final zig-zag cliff to Itea, then bumping our way along a rocky coast road around the west side of the bay to Galaxidhi. There or thereabouts, Comna assured us, we should find the handsome row of straight mature trees June was seeking to illustrate a point of Aristotelian theory; but again we drew blank, and were forced to pause for lunch. In the great days of sailing-ships and sea-captains, Galaxidhi had been a rich place, but its Byronic glory has departed, and most of the population with it, leaving behind a handsome port backed by the empty shells of nineteenth-century mansions and two or three fly-blown *tavernas*. Over lunch, we quizzed Comna about his life and job. He had fought with partisans and guerrillas of several political shades, right through to the end of the Civil War, and had taken up work afterwards as a truck-driver; but the bullet-wound in his head proved too disabling for him to maintain the necessary concentration and now, apart from a small pension, he had to find odd jobs for a living. Robbie, our production manager, who had been watching Comna a little quizzically, murmured to me that in his opinion Comna had chosen to accompany us 'not entirely for love', and I could see that our arrival had been a godsend to him. Still, there was no reason why he should not give us some solid help. Earlier he had taken a hand in beating down the olives; now we persuaded him to show us his skill with an axe, and as we drove back to Chrysso we enrolled him for our next main task.

*   *   *

All the major festivities of the Greek country year centre round a lamb-roasting, and nothing could be easier – Elias declared – than to lay on a lamb-roasting for us. If we simply guaranteed the price of the animal and the bundles of vine-cuttings for the fire, he would arrange the rest: we could make the fire at the foot of a particularly fine plane-tree which stood in the small square just below Mrs Bessie's house, across the way from the village school. We returned from Galaxidhi to keep this engagement, and were about to run our heads – though we could scarcely have guessed this – into a hornets' nest.

73

All over the world, small-town feuds and jealousies feed on the same trifling provocations. The lack of opportunities breeds officiousness, and this in turn begets self-importance, which begets touchiness. As a result, *la vie de province* exposes one to the continual risk of being struck down, not by the thunderbolt of Zeus, but by the frustrated pride of miniscule officialdom. In our case there was no reason to foresee trouble. Elias was one of the most respected men in the town, and what he sanctioned we need hardly feel anxious about. Skinned, prepared and spitted, the sacrificial lamb stood propped against the plane-tree. Comna bustled to and fro under Elias' direction, arranging the great bundles of vine prunings whose glowing ashes provide the chosen fuel for a Greek village barbecue. Fotis was attending to the final placing of the two camera tripods, while keeping at bay the growing crowd of curious school-children just out of class. Leaving them to finish these preparations, June and I slipped up to the house for some last pieces of equipment.

We were back within two minutes. The scene was transformed. From being calm and constructive, the atmosphere had become polarized, electric. The growing crowd had divided into two watchful halves. On one side of the scene, Comna was struggling and swearing, trying his hardest to break free from the grips of three onlookers. Elias, his dignity evidently ruffled, was fussing about ('*Po, po, po, . . .*'), in the hope of reducing the electric tension – whatever it was. Beside a fallen tripod, Fotis was hopping about, sucking his wrist and trying not to laugh too obviously. We were utterly mystified: however hot-headed Comna might be, surely he could not have picked a quarrel with the imperturbable Fotis in so extremely short a time. We hurried across the square. Fotis' first attempted explanations were inaudible, but we followed the jerk of his head towards the doorway of the school; and there we saw a new figure, who was clearly the other protagonist in the battle, grumbling to himself and adjusting a broken pair of gold-rimmed pince-nez on the bridge of his bloody nose.

'I tried to separate them': Fotis was at last intelligible. 'Him over there – something to do with the Town Hall. He tried to stop

Comna building the fire under the tree. Said the tree would be damaged, and was the property of the town. Comna was furious. You were strangers, English, honoured guests. You wanted a fire, and you should have a fire. The man tried to stop Comna lighting the fire. He says he only touched Comna's arm, but Comna went wild. Swears he gripped him by the shirt, was terribly offended, struck out at the man, would have torn him to bits if he hadn't been stopped.' We compared the sizes of the two of them: it must have been like a miniature poodle provoking an Alsatian. 'So of course we had to try and separate them, and d'you know what?' Fotis grinned, and held out his wrist. 'Comna was so angry he bit *me*!'

Slowly the emotional thunder began to subside. Our plan, however, had been quite disrupted. The friends of officialdom had sent for the local policeman: violence of this kind from a mere layabout could not be tolerated. Elias was conscious of an implicit affront to his own status; he reacted by drawing himself up, tense and pale, and muttering under his breath, '*Einai skata, einai skata.* . . . (The man's a shit . . .)'. Meanwhile, as his indignation slowly ebbed away, Comna was gradually being brought under control. When the policeman had arrived three minutes later, it was – fortunately – no longer necessary to keep him under actual physical restraint.

One can imagine an English policeman's report of the incident: 'Arriving on the scene, I took preliminary statements from both parties, before inviting them to accompany me to the station . . .': in other words, a fresh round of shouting broke out. The official swore This, Comna swore That. One Chorus, composed of friends of the official, confirmed This in unison. Elias, donning the air of an elder stateman, interposed that This was greatly exaggerated and one-sided; while the rival Chorus, friends of Comna, counter-asserted That. Comna himself was all oaths and fury, and rather too vehement for his own good, seeing that all the blood was on his fist: as the judicial procession set off down the steps – policeman, Comna, official and partisans of both sides – the law seemed definitely to be going against him. After a moment's reflection, Fotis set off to catch them up. Somebody not directly caught up in local jealousies should be there to see fair play.

We should clearly do no good by merely standing around the square, so we went along too, while Elias began disconsolately removing the disordered remnants of the unlit fire. 'Arrived at the station, I took a deposition from the complainant, who showed me his broken spectacles . . .': there was more vigorous shouting from behind the office door, as the two protagonists were interviewed in turn. June and I sat glumly in the outer office while the interrogation went on and on. The last raging of the argument rose and fell in the other room, like the distant growling of a retreating thunderstorm. After a quarter-of-an-hour the policeman came out, wiping his brow. Fotis rose and put on his most diplomatic tone. Might he introduce us . . .? And could he perhaps say something himself . . .? After all, he had – showing his wrist – been closely involved? Very well, the policeman conceded: he might speak. Ten minutes more and the outlines of an accommodation began to appear. Yes, agreed the arm of the law: there had been faults on both sides – and foolishness too. It was all most undignified and silly, especially in front of strangers and visitors. Neither protagonist had done himself any credit. They should both have had more pride, more self-respect, been less easily provoked. So the municipal official should not be encouraged to press his complaint: he himself would cut a pretty poor figure if he did. . . . The policeman ended reassuringly. We should leave it to him: matters could be adjusted.

We climbed the hill again up to the house, and let ourselves into the all-purpose outhouse. Elias was fully occupied restoring his own equanimity. We might be sure – he said, remembering his duty as our host – that the fire would be arranged: if not in the square then somewhere else, trust him. Across the room Bessie and Evthemia were soothing a grey-haired countrywoman, who was dabbing at her eyes and wailing: 'Oh dear, oh dear, always trouble. He is a good-hearted boy; he means well; but somehow, I am always anxious. . . .' Comna's mother wiped her eyes with her apron, her loving pride conflicting – not for the

76

first time – with shame and distress. Fotis explained how things were working out, and her anxieties began to subside. Half-an-hour later, having abandoned till tomorrow all thought of further filming, we set off in the car for Itea; and, as we drove past the front of the police-station, it looked as though the storm-clouds had finally blown away. For there, on a wrought-iron balcony overlooking the main street, the treaty of peace was being publicly ratified. Comna, the policeman and the municipal official were seated side by side in wicker chairs smoking, in formal testimony of this reconciliation. As we drove past, Comna's big head leaned over the balcony rail: he grinned down at us, waved and gave a broad wink.

Was the storm really over? Aeschylus would have known better. As we sat in the outhouse later that evening, Comna's complacent face came round the door. He let himself in and sat down. The pendulum had swung right over: anger and indignation had been given way to a certain pleased pride. In his moment of trial, he had not been found wanting: the rights of the strangers, the Nuffield, the English, had been assailed, and he, Comna, had stood up for them. He no longer remembered his narrow escape from the police-court, but recalled rather his staunch loyalty to our interests in the face of grave provocation. Elias was short with him, taking the longer view. This kind of thing might blow over temporarily, he remarked quietly, but Comna should not think that it would be forgotten. For the moment it might be forgiven but it would tell against him. Still, nothing more could be done to restore that situation: we must concentrate on more practical and immediate jobs. Comna sat back deflated, and Elias took over the conversation, explaining his revised plan for the lamb-roasting.

Next day he was as good as his word. The roasting went off without a hitch. The new location was a patch of waste land beside the olive-oil factory, at the very boundary between the village and the country-side. A shovel-full of squeezed olive-pulp served as the kindling, and soon the faggots of vine-prunings were flaring up noisily. We were impatient to put the lamb over the fire, but Elias warned us against doing this too soon. The fire must be allowed to die down, and the lamb cooked only over the embers. While we waited, Comna busied himself with making up the two Y-shaped supports which would support the shaft of the rotating spit at either end of the fire. After twenty minutes the vine-prunings had been reduced to a grey mound of ash, five feet long by eighteen inches wide; and Elias at last gave his consent for the lamb to be laid in position. Gripping the handle at one end of the spit, Comna began to rotate it smoothly and slowly. The intense heat rising from the vine cuttings (which, Elias explained, keep their heat remarkably fiercely and long) soon had its effect. Beads of liquid fat formed on the turning carcase and ran down its flank, to drop hissing into the ashes. Before long the wood-smoke acquired a new fragrance, and our mouths began to water.

As I knew very well already in theory, Aristotle's vision of nature had been strongly rooted in his interests as a naturalist. On this Earth of ours, he declared, nothing is as static, inert and unchangeable as – say – the patterns of the constellations, or the truths of mathematics. Everything in terrestrial Nature seems rather to be bound up in *processes*; not merely in processes, but in *cycles*; not merely in cycles, but in *life-cycles*. These life-cycles dictate the rhythm of Nature, and give the four seasons their goal. For they are not fruitless, purposeless cycles like the mere turnings of a wheel. Not at all: these are the rhythms of creation, which mark the unfolding, the coming-into-being, the fulfilment of Nature's own values. Instead of being vain repetitious turnings and returnings, Nature's fundamental life-cycles are all aimed and directed, all have a *hou heneka* (an 'in-aid-of-what'), are all *good for* something.

'Ah, the olive,' began Elias, giving practical expression to this rather abstract thought. Now that the roasting was safely under way, he could relax; and he stood there calmly, with no more than an occasional glance to make sure that the sacrificial victim – a four-month-old male – was kept turning at just the right speed and just the right height. There was a new light in his eyes, a new relaxed tone in his voice, and he was evidently speaking his deepest thoughts. 'The olive, you know, is a miracle. Yes, everything about the olive is miraculous. Everything about the olive is good. Everything about it is *for* something. The wood of the tree is a fine wood: hard, close-grained, moist, good for furniture and for axles, sturdy and strong. The fruit: you can eat the fruit as it is, and it will give you most things necessary for life, or instead you can crush the fruit and consume the oil.' A sun rose in his face as he thought of all the wonders and blessings conferred by olive-oil. 'But that is only the beginning. When you have taken the oil, do you have to throw the pulp away? Not at all: as you have just seen, it makes a wonderful fuel, and then. . .,' his normal gravity had given way to a new animation, and his voice rose as this encomium approached its climax: 'Do you know? *Even the ash* . . .' his voice dopped again dramatically and he leant forward, tapping me on the chest, 'even the ash from the burnt pulp makes an excellent *soap*.' He leant back again, and drew himself up with the air of one-who-knows, his left hand held up in bene-diction, the thumb and first finger just meeting. How better, he implied, to put oneself in tune with Nature than to enrol in the service of the Olive?

We had been looking forward with growing eagerness to getting our hands on the enticing carcase, just as soon as we could do so without burning our fingers. (Memories of Charles Lamb!) What, we thought, could be more delicious than hot fresh young roast lamb just off the spit? But Elias's authority was once again too much for us. We must wait, he said. In order to judge the true flavour, we must let it cool. So it was not until several hours later that we sat down to vast dishes of tepid, almost chilly meat, marvelling once again at that most eccentric feature of the *gout hellénique* – the taste for eating food half-cold. Comna had earned his share of the feast, and we all sat round a crowded table in the outhouse, picking over the dismembered carcase. Even though we poor uneducated heretics of English would gladly have eaten the meat a great deal hotter, it certainly had an excellent flavour. But at the end of a long day the quantity, especially of skin and fat, soon overcame us. June was the last to give up, struggling on bravely in response to the encourage-ments of Evthemia, who leant across the table and unearthed a

79

series of titbits from among the remains on her plate. 'Kalo,' she announced each time, 'Kalo;' and we all echoed the chorus inwardly: 'Kalo, Kalo ya to stomacha.'

After the meal, we all continued talking, and somehow the roast lamb induced a mood of reminiscence. Perhaps it was the associations of roast lamb. That was something Comna knew all about: for several years he had led a band of partisans, who had lived in the wild country above Delphi and Chrysso, roaming the maquis of Parnassus and the neighbouring mountains. No doubt, some of the sheep that disappeared into their stomachs were not, strictly speaking, their lawful property: but the partisans had to live somehow. Mrs Bessie, out of rivalry, decided to produce the certificate, sent to her by the British Embassy after the War, in acknowledgment of the help she had given to the Allied campaign, and for a few minutes there were raised voices and harsh words, as she hunted through her cupboards and desk-drawers trying to locate it. In the end it was she who wore Comna down, by launching into a long tale of the subterfuge and counter-subterfuge by which she had succeeded, single-handed, in outwitting the German commander at Desfina (which was her home village).

Yet it was Comna who produced the chief surprise of the evening. It came about in this way. Before leaving London we had been considering the possibility of recording in Greece some folk-music which we could use, free of copyright, on the sound-track of our completed film. The idea was possible, we were advised, but there were snags: one professional company filming in Cyprus had in fact been caught out disastrously. In a remote country bar one evening they heard a group of local bouzouki-players playing a catchy little tune. They leapt for their magnetic recorders, got the music safely on tape, and in due course had the satisfaction of putting out their documentary with a music-track absolutely out-of-copyright. A few months later the producer received a bill for £700 from a performing-rights agency: the 'folk-tune' in question, the accompanying letter pointed out, was recognizably an adaptation of the song 'She'll be coming round the mountain when she comes'. If we thought of going in for that kind of economy, we must therefore watch our step.

Comna had been telling us of the rivalry between the left-wing guerrillas and the right-wing guerrillas. Whenever two Greeks meet (it is said), they at once form three political parties; and the war against the Germans was complicated, and bedevilled, by fratricidal feuds and vendettas between the Greeks themselves. One of Comna's stories had distinctly Churchillian overtones. He and his team of left-wing partisans were running short of footwear – even of their favourite boots, which had soles and heels attached back to front, so as to confuse their enemies about whether they were coming or going. They turned to Jeff, their British liaison officer, and he promised to do his best. He radioed a message to Alexandria, and a few nights later a supply-plane dropped them a load by parachute. They unpacked it eagerly, only to find to their disgust that it contained 700 left boots without any right boots to match. Bitter and angry, they put Jeff up against a wall and threatened to cut his throat: what sort of allies were these? 'Wait a moment,' he replied. 'You will find that a corresponding load of right boots has been parachuted to the right-wing guerrillas on the next mountain. So, if you will just co-operate *for once*, you will end up with 350 perfectly good pairs of boots.'

'Boots!' Comna laughed, 'That reminds me . . .'; and he set off into a new string of stories about the end of the German War, and the Civil War that followed it. Why did they distrust the right-wingers? Well, he said, they had good reason to do so. Take the business of the UNRRA supplies – there was a racket for you. Why: everyone at the time was convinced that the Church was getting hold of the relief supplies and selling them at a profit. There was even a song about it. We egged him on a bit, hoping to get him singing. Did he play the *bouzouki*? No, but (he admitted) when he was a guerrilla he did sing and dance. Wouldn't he sing for us? Well, under pressure, he would tell us the *words* of the Unrra song. It went like this:

> Eipame pos tha moirasoun roucha,
> Kai papoutsia ap' ta mytera.
> E Em-El ta edhose sten Ounra,
> Ki' ap' ten Ounra kanane phtera.

Ta moirasan ste Thessalonike,
Kai ta moirasane kanonikos:
Dhyo atoma ena papoutsi,
Ki' ena maniki oikoyenniakos.

Robbie was chuckling loudly, and offered to translate the poem –
with a commentary – line by line.

It was said that they would distribute clothes,
And shoes with sharp-pointed (i.e. fashionable) toes.
Em-El (i.e. military liaison) gave them to Unrra,
And from Unrra they took wings (flew away).

They distributed them in Salonika,
They distributed them according to the rules:
One shoe for every two people,
And one sleeve (=foreskin) for each family.

But we were not to be put off. We clapped and cheered, hoping
to flatter Comna to a point at which he would consent to sing.
Finally he gave way: all right, then, if we insisted. . . . He launched
into a kind of clumsy, semi-musical declamation. We listened en-
tranced. Yes – no – it couldn't be – was it really? We made him
go right through the song again. This time there was no mis-
taking it: the music for the Unrra lampoon was an unmistakeable
relative of 'She'll be coming round the mountain'. The rhythm,
of course, had been disturbed to fit the words, some of the notes
were missing, some lengthened, some shortened, but the overall
effect was unquestionably the same. And, to this day, I can't
really decide whether that wretched film company *ought* to have
paid up the £700 for performing-rights. There may have been
plagiarism of some sort in the case, but perhaps the charge
should be 'returned to sender'. For did the Cypriot bouzouki-
players and the partisans of Parnassus alike incorporate the same
American pop-song into their repertory? Or was 'She'll be
coming round the mountain' itself the adaptation of a wide-
spread Greek folk-song? There's a subject for a Ph.D!

★   ★   ★

The second visit to Chrysso involved us – quite literally – in an unforeseen 'coincidence'. One part of our general plan was to visit not only Athens and the country-side of the mainland, but also a selection of the Aegean islands, and the Asiatic coastlands of Ionia around Miletus, where science was first born – and these are now part of Turkey. We had a lot of bulky equipment to carry around, and our itinerary would take us right across the normal shipping routes, so we ended by chartering our own transport – the 48-foot diesel-auxiliary yawl *Jack London* (Captain Tom Crichton, Master), registered at San Francisco but based in the Balearic Islands. Our rendezvous was to be at the Piraeus in the last days of March. Now, as we drove through Itea on the way to Desfina, we saw Cousin Louis wandering down the main street, looking more than ever like a piece of detached scar-tissue. He flagged us to a stop and announced: 'American yacht just come Itea.' Our eyebrows shot upwards. Its name? 'Not remember'; he scratched his head. 'Yes I think – *John London*.' We galloped down to the jetty, to find the yawl lying alongside the quay. It was in need of a lick of paint after its long haul from the Western Mediterranean, and at 10.30 a.m. there was no sign of life. We tried calling 'Hallo' and 'Ahoy there', and any other pieces of nautical slang that occurred to us. Surely Tom or Malcolm, his crew, or one of the passengers who had come along from Ibiza for the ride, must be on board and awake? Finally something stirred in the companionway, the sliding-hatch was pushed back, and an entirely unexpected figure appeared on deck. Bare feet, navy-blue serge trousers, a thick woollen sailor's jersey – that much was all very well. But the head! A young girl's face, oval, fine-proportioned, with classic features and a long mane of straight dark hair hanging loose down to her shoulders. Yes, she said, Tom was on board all right, and she'd give him a shout: a moment later, his familiar affable grin appeared above the hatch. He hastened to introduce us to Maureen, the ship's cook – 'and a very fine cook, too'. He suggested that she came along round the islands if that was all right with us. We were looking down at the hull, and he intercepted our glances. We weren't to worry about the paint: they would give her a com-

83

plete going-over the moment she reached Piraeus. 'See you later.'

On the morning of our last working day at Chrysso, I was fixing up some equipment (I forget what) in a corner of the town near the upper *plateia*. Far below, I had seen the white sails of the *Jack London* standing out across the bay on her first tack eastwards towards the Corinth Canal. After a while, an ancient taxi puffed its way up the hill and stopped. Cousin Louis got out and came across, a paper in his hand. What was it? I wondered. 'Very unfortunate, don't like to bother,' he began, thrusting the paper under my nose without any very obvious hesitation. 'American yacht gone without paying bill. As you friends of American yacht, I come consult you.' He had taken the precaution, he said, of telephoning the people at the Corinth Canal: that was this much (he pointed at the column of figures on his paper). Then there had been taxis: this much. And another phone-call to the Customs Office: this much. And then, of course, fifty drachmas for his own fees as Customs Agent . . . the whole thing came to somewhere around two pounds (or six dollars), so I decided that the easiest thing was to pay him off and be done with it. He clicked on a smile and retired to the taxi, the gold fillings in his molars glinting in the sunlight. With a last 'very unfortunate, sorry to bother' he was gone, and I turned back to my work. It must have mattered a lot to him (I thought) to make that journey up the hill from Itea, five miles each way. It was, of course, Tom's business whether or not he hired a Customs Agent, but he *had* happened to mention that they had signed in at Patras a couple of days earlier, so I wondered. A few days later, at the Piraeus, I quizzed him about it: 'What, that fellow?' he replied, 'not bloody likely!'

5 · Makers

—o❦·❧·❦❦·❧·❧o—

Under the moon, the shadows of the masts and rigging marched
slowly across the deck-timbers, slowed, halted, then began to
drift silently back again. The sea breeze had dropped at sunset,
and by now it was dead calm. Here off Serifos, some thirty miles
south-east of the point of Attica, the current was negligible, so
the boat could be left to sit quietly on the water through the
night with only one person keeping watch on deck. We had been
lucky in our first day's sailing, coasting down from Piraeus to
Sounion in bright sunshine – at first under power, but later
sailing in a pleasant breeze – before making away from the
mainland, S 33°E, into the islands. By evening everyone was
settling in, the last of the heavy equipment was stowed away, and
when I went below at nine o'clock for a sleep the sound of a
Beethoven 'cello sonata was coming over Fotis's transistor radio
from Athens. 'When I had a flower-shop on Sixth Avenue,'
began Robbie (the gambit was worthy of Stephen Potter): he
had looked round at us all, as we sat on deck before lunch eating
from a plate of sardines and olives, while in the background a
soprano voice had floated over us from the radio. 'Why yes,' he
went on, 'one of my best clients was Lily Pons.'

For my own part, I can never think of settling down to ten
hours' solid sleep the first night on board a new boat; so I volun-
teered gladly for the post of night-watchman. At 1 a.m. I took
my sleeping-bag on deck, and rolled up under the rail. For a
couple of hours I dozed on and off, while Fotis sat keeping the
look-out from the cockpit. From where I lay, he was no more than
a silhouette against the diffuse light of the night sky, his face lit
from time to time by a rosy circle as he drew on his cigarette.
Nothing else stirred: when he tapped the ash off his cigarette,

85

one could hear it land on the deck. Then he turned in, and I was alone. For a while the lightest breath of wind got up, wrinkling the flat surface of the sea in every direction and breaking the moon's track into a million random drops. Then it fell calm again. Drifting at a fraction of a knot, the boat continued to swing gently under the moon – five degrees to port, then five degrees to starboard. Once a high-flying aeroplane went over, its triangle of lights (red, white and green) disappearing down the line of islands in the direction of Crete. Once there was the distant murmuring of engines from an inter-island steamer, a minute caterpillar of lights crawling its way along the northern horizon. Otherwise silence.

The three chief objectives of our voyage were Crete, Samos and the Ionian mainland; but, along the sides of our triangular course, there lay half-a-dozen other islands of interest for our inquiries. We had been hoping, for example, to discover – and film – a potter who was still working according to the old craft-techniques. For the early Greeks had not been mere observers of nature, who stood back passively and philosophized in the abstract about a universe they were powerless to control. On the contrary: theirs was a world in which everyone knew something of the practical arts, and was familiar with certain basic craft-processes. Maybe the philosophers were not themselves crafts-men, since in classical Athens the world of learning was largely a preserve of 'gentlemen-scholars'. Yet no one could have lived in an ancient Greek town without seeing, every day of the week, something of the traditional craft-procedures that potters, metal-workers, dyers and glassmakers had been developing around the Eastern Mediterranean ever since 4000 B.C. or before.

Traces of this familiarity with the arts and crafts are apparent even in the earliest of their scientific speculations. For one finds the first Greek scientists using models drawn from this craft-world to explain the world of Nature: seeing the clouds, for instance, as forming out of the air by 'felting'. I recalled the old Muslim craftsman whom I had seen at work in his booth in the market-square at Peč – a town in southern Yugoslavia, not far from the Albanian border, where there were (he said) 'four

86

Muslims for every Serb' – how he took a translucent and in-substantial handful of lambs' wool, soaped it, beat it, squeezed it, pressed it, folded it and shaped it, until it became a hard, solid, opaque, white felt skull-cap. Aristotle, in the same way, came to the processes of Nature, not just with a naturalist's dispassionate interest in life-cycles and animal behaviour, but with a deeper theoretical concern: the growth and self-perfection of the developing organism had, in his view, much in common with the elaboration of a work of art under the craftsman's hands – except that in the case of the organism the workman and his work were one and the same. 'We tend to overlook this likeness,' he re-marked, in a penetrating aside, 'through taking it for granted that in all creation there must be – say – both a boatbuilder *and* a boat, and that these must be *separate*. But this is not necessarily so: *A doctor doctoring himself* – that is what Nature most resembles.' And, in time, the whole Greek system of thought about the material constitution of things came to be organized around one central idea; that natural objects originate from the four ele-ments by a process of mixing, blending and compounding – a natural 'concoction' comparable to those engaged in by cooks and craftsmen. Bearing all this in mind, June was planning to build her finished film around an Aristotelian skeleton: linking to-gether all her visual demonstrations of the thought-patterns which the different Greek scientists brought to their interpretation of the world, by relating them all to the making of a pottery vase. This vase would do duty as a visual symbol of the whole World of Nature, and she would begin expounding each type of theory from some point connected with the potter's craft – the in-gredients of the vase (say), or the mathematical proportions of its form, or the functions it would perform when completed.

* * *

Our two first reconnaissances had been abortive, and we were hoping that, when we called next day at the island of Sifnos, it would be a case of 'third time lucky'. 'All the chamber-pots of Athens are produced in Sifnos,' Robbie had assured us; and he had promised to find out more precisely where the factory in question was located.

We had started by trying Aegina, the triangular island halfway across the Saronic Gulf between Athens and the Peloponnese. Gregory, our friend in the Prime Minister's office, was sure we should find everything we wanted there, and in any case (he insisted) the island itself was one we absolutely must visit; it was a wonderful island, wonderful; he was himself a native of Aegina, and liked nothing better than revisiting it. He would telephone to his cousin to expect us. So early one morning, shortly after our return from Vytina and Chrysso, we presented ourselves at the Piraeus, in time to catch the boat for Aegina and points beyond. There was the usual flurry of hens in crates, old men with bulging sacks, young men carrying brown paper parcels, and tearful relatives. A microbus from one of the posh hotels decanted a party of Anglo-Saxons off for a day-trip to Hydra and, when we came round to the front of the promenade deck, we found them firmly installed and in loud conversation. There was a genteel Australian, in a blue blazer; there was a gushing lady in tweeds and brogues, who was exclaiming about her livestock ('Oh my dear, Ayrshires! They're terribly, terribly sweet to human beings, but they're simply *beastly* to each other . . .'); and there was also the very model of a retired Army Officer, with tortoiseshell spectacles and a closely-trimmed moustache which failed to conceal two front teeth that had not been properly repressed in his teens. He was dressed in cavalry-twill trousers and discreetly-checked jacket, moss-green porkpie hat, and pale suede shoes with rubber golfing soles. His beige tie was dotted with a small brown lozenge motif, and his long-sleeved Jaeger pullover was buttoned down the front.

Occidental dress in a very different style was awaiting us on the quayside at Aegina. We fought our way down the gangplank and looked around the quay for Gregory's cousin. There were two priests in stovepipe hats, a couple of dozen countrywomen, several men who had already recognized their friends and relations, and a young girl with long, mousy hair, wearing grey flannel trousers and a tight mauve sweater, check bobbysocks and slip-on casual shoes. It took us both some time to make the connection. She was looking for an irretrievably middle-aged party: we were looking for someone *male*. (Q: 'The Little Indian was the Big Indian's son; what relation was the Big Indian to the Little Indian? A: *Mother*' – this trap no longer works if you replace 'Indian' by 'Frenchman' or 'Scotsman'.) But the girl was indeed Gregory's cousin; it was very nice – *très aimable* – of him to send us to Aegina; they often wished that he would come himself – he had not been back for ten years (!); though she of course often went to Athens, and had in fact recently returned from the Sorbonne. But we must sit down and have a drink, and in a few minutes there would be a bus across to the temple on the other side of the island.

It was one of those days when good resolutions are side-tracked from the word Go. We diffidently raised the question of potteries. Oh yes, there were potteries: she waved her hand towards a pile of coarse yellow souvenirs ('Presents from Aegina') in front of a quayside shop. But first she must take us to the temple. We let ourselves be diverted into one of the island buses which gave three loud, experimental coughs, and then set off jerkily inland. The temple was at the north-east corner of the island, standing on a prominent ridge and surrounded by pine trees. The bus dropped us at the foot of the hill, and we walked up a rough road which petered out into a sandy track just near the temple: to the south the land dropped away steeply towards a beautiful cove, and north from the temple there was a view clear across the sea to Attica. We clambered around the elegantly restored ruins with dutiful exclamations, ate the local pistachio nuts, and made one quickly frustrated attempt to break away. Surely we could manage a good old English-style tramp through the pine-woods, and across country down to the road again; but Greg's cousin was a more careful shepherdess than Mrs Bessie had been. We had gone only 150 yards before she noticed which way we were going. She started after us. Her thin Parisian shoes were not made for running, and threatened to trip her, but she called and called until we had to stop, and permit ourselves to be redirected down the road by which we had come. When we reached the nearest village, it was after midday. Two minute black lambs were tied by a rope to the doorway of the local bar. We were just embarking on glasses of the local orange-squash when a metallic clanking from up the road announced the return of the bus; so we had to gulp, run, and shoe-horn our way back on board. Held together by rust and faith, and by medallions of St Christopher, the B.V.M. and the local patron St Nektandos (who qualified for no less than five ikons), the machine wheezed and freewheeled its way back to the town.

We raised again the question of the potteries. Lunch, she said, lunch was the first thing. We bowed to her authority, not unwillingly by this time. The meal was leisured and prolonged, and after it she excused herself: she had a job at the school on several afternoons each week, so she must leave us, but if we really wanted to find the potteries we need only ask – there would be no difficulty. . . . By now, however, we were overfed, and the little port was wrapped in the silence of its siesta. June and I explored the headland to the north of the harbour. Small blue irises were growing wild under the trees; and, when we clambered down to the shore, we found a sheltered corner where the sun was hot enough on the shallow water for the first bathe of the season. By the mid-afternoon the life of the town was only just beginning again and the return boat to Athens picked us up with our mission entirely unfulfilled. All we had seen at Aegina of pottery was a row of pointed amphoras, lying beside a cottage at the country village. Yet from these we had at any rate learned one thing: that impractical-looking shape, with the body of the jar carried down all the way from the shoulders to the sharp point in one long straight line, was not so foolish after all. Indoors, one could set it upright only by placing it on a metal stand; but here the jars were lain in rows on the bare earth, and their long flanks provided a stable base on which they stood securely, with their open necks facing upwards.

The coast of Aegina retreated behind us, and merged gradually into the snow-capped silhouette of the Peloponnese, whose topmost ice-sheets were opalescent under the setting sun. We were tempted to mutter 'sour grapes', dismissing the pottery of Aegina as coarse and crude, so as to excuse ourselves for being so completely seduced from our search: 'Tomorrow,' we promised ourselves, 'tomorrow we would go to Maroussi.' This was the suburb on the northern outskirts of Athens where, Robbie told us, many of the most typical potteries were concentrated. Out there, perhaps, we should find what we wanted.

Next day at Maroussi we did have one stroke of luck: unfortunately, we were in need of two. The road out from the centre of Athens and through the northern suburbs is a dual-carriageway affair, whose merits as a highway have been partly cancelled out by the ribbons of suburban development which have formed on either side. (It reminded us more than anything of the Great West Road out of London.) Some twenty minutes from the centre we reached signs announcing 'Amaroussion', and here Fotis told us to slow down. For although, in the everyday language of Greece, everyone *calls* the suburb Maroussi, it goes by a longer and grander name in the 'official' language – that cultural albatross which the Greeks have hung round their own necks, to satisfy the same motives of historical status-seeking as the Erse alphabet of modern Ireland. Evidences of the local industry became apparent at once. Row upon row, the local counterparts of garden gnomes were lined up to catch the eye of the passing motorist. Water-jars and flower-pots stood in carefully posed groups, like so many football-teams awaiting the photographer. Some of them were in simple red fired clay, but many were decorated with crude mosaic designs made up from brightly glazed tesserae. Here and there, the craftsman had caught and reproduced an authentic ultramarine of the traditional Turkish shade, but in almost every display the elegant virtues of the ancient forms were hidden beneath a cosmetic layer of twentieth-century bad taste.

The apparent contrast between form and decoration could, of course, be misleading. One has to apply contemporary canons of taste to the surviving products of ancient art and craftsmanship with great caution. The sublime marble statues of antiquity, impeccable in the snowy purity of their anatomical form, have imposed on Europeans during the last four centuries a conception of what is highest in the sculptural arts quite foreign to the actual practices of classical Greece. Like the cult of 'old masters' – in which a blend of dirt and ageing varnish narrows the range of visible colours into a restricted spectrum of greens, browns and olives – the worship of the unadorned stone figure as the supreme form of sculpture has grown up from a study of art-objects in a state of decrepitude. In most cases, the colourless marble limbs which are all that have survived their centuries of interment, to reappear under the archaeologist's spade, were only a first foundation: the completed statue was coloured in flesh-tones, equipped with glinting eyes, and even clothed and bejewelled. So perhaps it would be premature to credit the early Greeks with a positive *preference* for undecorated pottery, in which nothing could distract the eye from the beauties of geometrical form. Certainly the bulk of their pottery was like that; but that may well have been for reasons of economic necessity. After all, the bulk of our own twentieth-century table china is similarly devoid of gold-leaf, and it has been one of the curses of industrial design during the last century that bad taste can now be indulged *cheaply*.

We had no particular reason to start our exploration in one workyard rather than another. So we parked the car, and wandered along the verge of the road, looking for the display that contained the fewest gnomes and mosaics. A hundred yards or so along was a yard containing almost entirely bare brown pottery in a variety of shapes, decorated at most with simple waving lines of white glaze. We stepped inside and began looking along the rows of pots, in the hope of finding reproduced something approaching the full riches of the ancient forms. A bare-footed young man in khaki shirt and trousers, with a moustache and short, bristly hair, came out from the buildings behind the yard. They had a wider selection of pots inside, if we would care to look. We followed him into the dusty interior of the workshops, and found stacks of pottery at every stage of production, from the raw materials in the courtyard (tanks of water and piles of dry, crumbly clay) to the soft shapes carefully stacked within the workshop oven waiting for the fire to be lit in the furnace below. None of it, however, had quite the character we were looking for. What exactly did we want then? the young man asked. 'Have you any ancient shapes?' asked Fotis. 'No, not here,' he replied. 'But next door,' he added at once, 'there is a man who is an archaeologist.'

He led us round the back of the workshop into the neighbouring courtyard, and in through the door of a small room. Here we found, not an archaeologist, but something better – a craftsman who was still making, for his own satisfaction, pots whose forms were deliberately based on the classical Greek styles of pottery. At a table in the window sat a young girl shaping handles, and fitting them to pots which were nearly ready for firing. In the far corner of the room was a simple wheel which was driven, not mechanically, but merely by thrusting with the foot on a small disc at the botton of the axle. The potter himself came forward. His name, he said, was Ioannes Dhelavinias: it is preserved for us in the imprint of the small seal with which he signs his products. The nature of his work explained the roughness of his clothes – thick army shirt, aged buff cardigan, carpet slippers, and coarse khaki trousers worn through into holes – but his manner was distinguished and reserved, almost scholarly.

The conversation began slowly but we could see the perfectionist craftsman in Fotis warming to a fellow perfectionist. Ioannes Dhelavinias was delighted that anyone should share his enthusiasm for these beautiful *archaiai morphai*, and nothing gave him more pleasure than to show off the products of his research. Here for instance was a *kratera*, a flat mixing jar or punch-bowl in which the wine was diluted, blended and mixed at table. And these, here, were amphorae of the genuine archaic shape – the rugged jars in which wine was stored or transported in bulk by sea or land: look at the sturdy carrying-handle, and the narrow neck which could be easily stoppered and sealed. And that broad-mouthed vase to the right in a deeper red, with three small handles and a decorative black rim: that was his version of the famous *kokkino* of Samos, which became so popular among the Romans that they took over the technique for themselves, and made 'red Samian ware' all over their Empire. He was just about the only living person who knew the secret of that glaze, and how to get the superimposed black glaze to take on top of it, all at a single firing. Next door, there: that was a really big amphora, badly cracked. Firing these large pots was not easy: if the cooling was not controlled *just so*, all his earlier care could go for nothing. As to the rest – he waved his hand along the shelves – there were a lot of little things he had turned out . . . nothing of any significance.

We gazed at the beautiful objects in a state of . . . well, some frustration. In so many ways, he was exactly our man. He could make, was making every day, the very sort of vase or pot that would serve ideally the symbolic task June had in mind for it. And yet . . . looking round his workshop, we could see that filming him at work would be a fiendish business. His wheel was fixed permanently in a constricted corner of the room. Instead of daylight, we should have to rig up artificial light; and, even so, it would be no easy job to get an adequate overall level of lighting, without the potter himself casting deep shadows all over his work. We might yet be compelled to do our work this way, but it would (we thought) be decidedly a second-best: in the meanwhile, however, we must certainly ask him to make us one of his pots for use elsewhere in the film.

Why, of course: he would do so with pleasure. We need only tell him which shape we should prefer. As he did not have a complete selection on view, we could look at some photographs of his other styles. He went to the table and started thumbing through some pictures. Oh, that man? – he was holding an ancient photograph of a middle-aged man with close-cropped hair, and wearing a running-vest – that was a fellow-villager of his, who had won the Marathon race (or rather failed to win it through missing the last lap) at the first modern Olympic Games, held at Athens in 1896. Dhelavinias had known him well: he had been a wonderful old man, and at the age of sixty-five could still outrun everyone else in the village. The next photograph showed us the Greek royal family at an art-exhibition: the King was presenting a prize to a well-turned-out man, with a neatly-trimmed moustache and an elegant lounge suit. 'Yes, that's me . . . and here,' he turned over quickly to the remaining photographs, 'are some of the pots that won me the prize.'

We ended by ordering two of the large amphorae, one of them capable of standing on its own, the other ending in the typical long point: the potter would get a circular wrought-iron stand made up for us by a friend down the road. But we had to understand, he emphasized, that these really large pots were always a bit chancy. We weren't to worry: if they did not come out right, he would not dream of charging us. But though he would do his best, he could not guarantee results. Anyway let us come back in a fortnight and see how things were getting on. Fotis sounded him, delicately, about prices. The potter meditated a moment, then named a figure which seemed to us ridiculous – ridiculously low, that is. We po-po-ed his suggestion, complaining that he was robbing himself. But no (he said), that was his price. True: there had been one Frenchman who spent the whole afternoon bargaining with him for a whole collection of his pots, and who, when he had offered to sell the lot for 500 drachmas, had insisted on paying a 'bargain price' of 900. But please (he added): we were not to embarrass him by trying to pay more than he asked; and meanwhile (by this time we were moving towards the door) he asked us to accept, as a present, this small jar – he took down a little deep-red-glazed jug from a shelf and turned it upside down – with his name stamped on the base.

* * *

That was how things stood when we joined the *Jack London*. When we returned to Athens after the boat trip we might yet have to go back to Maroussi and film our pottery sequence there. Meanwhile, Sifnos was only a little way across the water. From where I sat on deck, wrapped in my sleeping-bag, the silhouette of Serifos lay against the night-sky immediately behind me. I followed the lights of a second aeroplane overhead, until it disappeared behind the rugged outline of the island. It was still barely four in the morning: one could make out only a darker shadow pasted on to the charcoal background of the sky. Rather

95

to the left of centre, the top of the silhouette seemed – mysteriously – to be snow-covered under the moonlight: elsewhere, it was the purest black. Further to my right, a smaller and more distant silhouette must be Sifnos itself. Otherwise, from horizon to horizon, the dome of the sky was filled by the moon and stars alone. Slowly and gently, the boat continued swinging.

The passage of time showed first in the appearance of the moon. Before there was any visible trace along the eastern horizon, a sickly lemon tinge began to tarnish its face. As the contrast gradually increased, the patch of 'snow' on Serifos acquired a new luminosity. Then, in the East, a first streak of green, broken by black cloudlets, framed the top edge of the sea. Paling against the first light of morning, a second inter-island steamer crept eastward into the coming dawn. New island silhouettes formed on the horizon, as the spectrum of light broadened gradually from the indigo of night through the first green to an incandescent lemon. For a while, the line of clouds still lay dark across this spectral background. Then the base of the furthest clouds, touched by the first fiery red of the day, suddenly caught alight. Like the draught of a furnace, the hot breath of the sun fanned the fire; the conflagration spread along the line of clouds, until they were all aflame; then the furnace of the sky blazed up more and more violently, until the whole substance of the upper aether seemed to be at white heat.

Day had come. The top of the world was filled once more with its own proper element – Fire. I rolled the top of the sleeping-bag down my chest, and stretched my arms above my head. Here was a good omen: Nature was once again showing herself as the ancient Greeks had seen her, undisguised by the intellectual veils of modern theory. I rolled over on my front: Serifos had become a three-dimensional rocky mass, rising out of the dark sea and topped, not by snow, but by a whitewashed mountain village. Yes; and there, way ahead to starboard, was Sifnos.

Maureen's dark mane of hair appeared above the hatch, and with silent gestures we exchanged the watch. Half-asleep in the cabin below, I was vaguely conscious of the diesel engine being started, and a couple of hours later I came up on deck to find the

Jack London rounding the westernmost headland of Sifnos. By now the sea had recovered its normal daytime blue, and the rough grass sloping down to the cape was overlaid with a pink wash of spring flowers. Another mile along the coast, and the ship was abeam of a lighthouse. Immediately beyond, we turned into a narrow creek. It was unclear, from our chart, whether we were entering the cove of Pharos, or that of Platy Yialou, where there was rumoured to be a pottery. Behind the shelter of the headland three cheerfully-painted caiques swung at anchor, and we came up alongside. Promisingly enough, the nearest boat was laden with pottery of some kind or other – though not the expected chamber-pots. Beyond the caiques was a small landing-stage and a settlement of three houses, from which a stone-flagged path could be seen starting its way inland up a small valley. And even from our anchorage we could see small purple irises dotted over the rocky slopes to within a few feet of the sea.

After a minute a white dinghy started out from the shore. A young man in his mid-twenties stood up in it, and called out to us as he backwatered: 'Let us know if you want anything.' We waved him to come on board, and offered him a cigarette. He thanked us civilly but declined, jerking his head towards the landing-stage. His father (he explained) ran the bar on the quay, and would not allow him to smoke. Yes: this was Pharos, and Platy Yialou was another half-mile on, the other side of that headland with the little chapel. Certainly there were potters working at Platy Yialou. He, Petros, would be happy to take us round there – just give him five minutes to row ashore, and make sure it was all right with Father.

He was soon back, and we set off again under his guidance. Once we had gone half-way across from the landing-stage to the headland of Chrysopigi, Petros was ready to accept a cigarette. He was, he admitted, nearly thirty: his father didn't *like* his smoking, but of course . . . – he shrugged his shoulders. Pointing to a crack which cut off the very end of the headland from the main body of the island, he told us of the local legend. Two of the island women, it was said, had been saved from pirates by the timely intervention of the local Saint, who responded to their prayers by opening up that crack in the rocks and so isolating the raiders from the island. The chapel had been built to commemorate this miracle. Was there anything in the story? Petros would not care to say.

We swung round, keeping well clear of the cape, and came in sight of the bay beyond. It had a wide and open beach, unprotected from the sea but safe enough to land from a dinghy on such a calm day. At Pharos we had been in a crook of the rocks, where the stony fingers of the mountainous island enclosed a small corner of sea. Here at Platy Yialou the shore was more like the palm of a hand: for once, a small pocket-handkerchief of hinterland ran back between the broad beach and the foot of the main hills. At the western end of the beach there was a little group of houses, and this, Petros told us, housed the pottery.

We anchored and rowed ashore. Just beyond the first house on the left was a low white building, which was the potters' chief workshop. A gross of newly-shaped casseroles was laid out in rows between the shed and the square furnace-house next to it. Two men were lifting them, one by one, and swilling a spoonful of glaze round the interior of each pot in preparation for the final firing. They paused at their work, straightened up, and directed us into the workshop where we found the chief craftsman at his wheel. He was taller than Dhelavinias, and his output was evidently much more orthodox; yet he had some of the same distinction, the same reflective air of a man who sets himself his own exacting standards of work. For a moment our hearts fell. Though the room was a great deal lighter than the workshop at Maroussi, the wheel was once again set up indoors, in a rather constricted position – against the inner wall and beside a bench, above which hung a cheap calendar, a telephone and a single electric light-bulb, attached (it appeared) to no supply of current.

We explained our problem, fencing around it diplomatically. The potter pushed back his cloth cap and smiled knowingly. Something could be managed, he thought, though he wasn't sure if it would work. Still, if we cared to make the experiment, it might be possible to improvise a wheel out on the flagged area between the workshop and the beach. We leapt at the suggestion and divided up our party, one half rowing back to J. L. to collect the cameras and equipment, the others setting themselves to prepare a position for the wheel.

Over the next five hours, the potter gave us a demonstration of his whole art, up to a point just short of the furnace. He showed us how the rough clay was crumbled and sieved, to form a fine, uniform dust; how, kneeling beside a tank of water, he gradually blended the sieved clay into a wet and glutinous lump; and – most impressively – how this lump finally took shape under his hands, as his bare foot kept the wheel turning rhythmically on its axle. In a corner of his workshop, we had noticed a very handsome waterjug, with a narrow neck and a pattern of decorative stars. At our request, he now set out to reproduce from the raw clay, as nearly as he could, a vase having the same basic shape. This time, however, we had two cameras running throughout the whole process – one catching the scene as he twirled the axle with his foot, carefully and slowly throwing the wet clay up into the shaft of the neck; the other playing in close-up on the mass of clay itself, and recording the gradual transformation which his delicate fingers imposed on it. So, on the beach at Sifnos, the whole philosophical conception of 'form' being imposed on 'matter' took on a new realism and relevance for us.

By four o'clock we had all that we absolutely needed, and the sky was hazing up badly. Our friend the potter was outside, dismantling the improvised wheel, when the telephone rang in the workshop. Fotis answered it: 'Legete? . . .' He listened: 'Socrates? . . .'. Somebody called Socrates was wanted on the phone. The potter came in and took the earpiece. We had a last look round the workshop, half unwilling to leave, but when he had hung up it was time to say Good-bye. He was unwilling to take a penny for his day's labours. Under pressure he would agree only to accept 100 drachmas as payment for the decorative water-pot, which he himself valued at only 10 – i.e. half-a-crown, or 30 cents. Beyond that he would take nothing from us, and declared smilingly that he had enjoyed the day.

We took a farewell glance at the furnace. The classical Greeks' experience of Fire was, evidently, not confined to observation. Ever since the legendary Prometheus had brought a stolen sample of the Heavenly Fire down to earth, men had used Fire, mixing it as an ingredient into their artefacts and imitating for themselves the natural effects they could see produced under their eyes by the heat of the sun. Thus, our potter had begun by mixing Water and Earth: having shaped his pot, he placed it in the oven and exposed it to the heat of the furnace. In this way, the finished product seemed to embody also the Air and Fire which went into the process of baking. And how soon – how pitifully soon – we allow ourselves to become scornful of discredited ideas. True: the cosmological idea of Fire, as forming the uppermost layer of the astronomical universe, was swept away at the very beginning of the seventeenth century. One finds John Donne, for instance, lamenting the break-up of the familiar earth-centred picture of the cosmos:

> And new Philosophy calls all in doubt,
> The Element of fire is quite put out;
> The Sun is lost, and th' Earth, and no man's wit
> Can well direct him where to looke for it.
> And freely men confess that this world's spent
> When in the Planets, and the Firmament
> They seeke so many new; then see that this
> Is crumbled out againe with his Atomies.
> 'Tis all in peeces, all Cohaerence gone;
> All just supply, and all Relation.

But, though the Element of Fire might be put out of the sky, it kept a respected place in physics and chemistry for a further 200 years. Not until the eighteen-fifties did men at last have sufficient reasons for setting aside finally the older view of fire and heat as the effects of a tenuous, but nevertheless material substance.

Our day at Sifnos had one last postscript. Behind the furnace-room there was a store-room, and before leaving we just glanced inside. There one last surprise was waiting: as well as hundreds of casseroles and water-pots, it contained about a dozen large storage jars, five or six times the height of anything we had seen at Maroussi. In their scale, shape and decoration, they resembled nothing in my experience except the jars one sees in archaeological photographs of the palace at Knossos in Crete. These were no mere bins for a few pounds of sugar or flour: each of them would easily have accommodated one of Ali Baba's Forty Thieves. It would have been interesting to stay ashore longer, but the weather was rapidly worsening and we had to go. Nor could there be any real question of our transporting one of these great jars all the way round the Aegean undamaged. Still: the day was ending, as it had begun, with a favourable omen. The ancient world significantly regarded their craftsmen as having learned their arts ultimately from demi-gods; and here we had found some of the evidence we were seeking that the craft-traditions of present-day Greece stretched back continuously, not just for decades or centuries, but for millennia – beyond the whole classical era to the Minoan world which, for us today, stands at the very fringe of history, on the borderline between the light and the dark.

6 · A. and M.

—◦❧ ⊰⊱◦❧◖◗⊰⊱◦ ❧◦—

Our experiences were beginning to fall into a pattern. We had come to Greece hoping to reconstruct for ourselves something of the origin of Greek science: either by discovering traces of earlier systems of thought lingering on into the present day, or by bringing the classical ideas back to life for ourselves in the environment of their birth. The first of these hopes had always been rather a desperate one: almost universally, modern education has been fatal to traditional systems of thought, and no 'modern man' cares to profess an idea which he has once learned to regard as 'superstitious'. Yet, though the ideas of classical Greek science might play no part in the conscious convictions of Greeks today, we still had the other line of evidence to explore – and this was proving far from fruitless. Though the older ideas had been over-run and smothered by the more vigorous growths of modern science, the soil from which they sprang was still there. Here and there, indeed, we had even come across an intellectual seedling or two left over from that earlier stock.

The positive clues had been of two kinds. Some of them had come from everyday experience – from simply looking at Nature with unsophisticated eyes, and observing for ourselves things which the men of the Aegean have always had there to see. Others had turned up as soon as we left the twentieth-century environment of Athens, and exposed ourselves to earlier modes of life. We ourselves could recognize, just as the ancient Greeks had done, the likeness between the fire in the sky and the fire in the potter's kiln. The stratification of the universe – its four-fold division into the fiery heavens, the circumambient air, the waters of the sea, and the all-supporting earth – was for us no longer a theoretical hypothesis, but a fact of simple observation. To the working craftsman, also, these four elements were no theory, still less a superstition: they were a practical necessity. In order to make a pot, one must ensure supplies of four different kinds – Earth in the form of clay, Water to bind it, and finally, Fire and Air mixed in due proportions so as to produce the intense and penetrating heat needed to bake it through and through. The cyclical transformations of Nature were evident equally to the watcher and to the doer. The motions of the heavens, 'framed by the Creator' (as Plato put it) 'to be as nearly perfect as such material things can be', span delicate variations year by year out of the same fundamental themes, which followed one another as season succeeded season like the bells in a complicated peal. So much could be seen by anyone who took the trouble to look. But those whose livings depended on understanding Nature more intimately could go further: for them, Nature was 'cyclical', not just in a mathematical sense – repeating her appearances in due numerical succession – but also in a more profound, organic sense. Birth and growth proceeded in step with the cosmic seasons, according to the patterns of their own 'life-cycles'. Thus sun and stars, sheep and olives, were woven together (or so experience suggested) into a single fabric, with its own characteristic, circular weave.

Indeed, if looked at from this particular point of view, the ideas of our own, more recent science might well come to appear excessively abstract and remote. When we say that modern science is 'experimental', we put on record two quite different truths. Since 1600, scientists have made it a point of method, of principle, even of pride, to accept a novel theory or hypothesis only after checking all its implications for themselves. This much is to the good; yet we must remark that this process of checking, which is crucial for modern science, *has* to be 'experimental' in another sense also, for one very particular reason. The soundness of the ideas at the foundation of modern science is far from apparent to common observation – one would never arrive at them on the basis of obvious, everyday experience alone. Common observation shows us that solid bodies fall to the earth and come rapidly to rest, unless kept forcibly in motion: without a highly sophisticated study of all the factors involved, men would never have hit on the modern conception of 'inertia'. And, if the concepts and theories of modern science are 'mechanistic', this is not merely because the scientists concerned arbitrarily chose to frame them in terms of mechanical analogies; but because, in the last two centuries, the mechanical arts of modern engineering have been carrying us all beyond, and behind, the less sophisticated techniques of the traditional crafts.

All the same, while the older intellectual constellations might be low in the sky, they were not yet completely eclipsed. Earlier craft-traditions and modes of life co-exist with twentieth-century society and technology, and the corresponding attitudes of mind co-exist also. So we were beginning to see, not just the outlines of the older patterns, but also how they are related to the more modern ones. When Francis Bacon was first faced with the Copernican account of the planetary system, he was not (I recalled) just *dubious* about it: he was positively *mystified*. For, from one point of view, the new theory simply could not be right. To say that the sun stood still contradicted what everyday experience confirmed – that the sun starts the day by rising above the horizon, then moves across the sky to the zenith, and finally sinks below the western horizon again. This was not (as I now saw) a *silly* reaction. On the contrary: to understand how the theories of modern science are related to Nature, one must recognize that this contradiction is illusory, so that it can be true, at the same time, *both* that the Sun rises and moves across the sky *and*, in another sense, that the Earth is moving, rather than the Sun. For, in unravelling these illusory contradictions, we come to understand better the reasons why, in order to fathom and manipulate the workings of Nature, we need a 'theory' at all – how, for instance, behind the growth of the Copernican system, lay a new scientific ambition: not simply to keep a mathematical tally of the celestial appearances, but actually to devise a single, consistent mechanical model which would display the planetary motions as a *system*. (The key step in constructing such a model is, of course, to put the Sun at the centre of the planetary system, and to arrange for the earth and the other planets to move around it.)

Sciences, A. & M. – Ancient and Modern, and at the same time Agricultural and Mechanical: that was how the contrast was beginning to appear. But would the same pattern persist? Ten days later, in the remote countryside of eastern Crete, this contrast was to be burned into our minds as the result of a bizarre coincidence.

*   *   *

Between Sifnos and Crete, there lie 120 miles of sea. The line joining them passes near only one significant landmark, the island of Thera, or Santorini. This island is the most curious of all the Cyclades: around it there hangs, not just a cloud of sulphurous vapours, but also a haze of legends, half-memories and speculations. Even if it had not been a natural stepping-stone upon our route, the mysterious reputation of Santorini would have done a lot to draw us there.

For something – something quite horrific – happened at Santorini, just before the beginning of history. The collective memories of the Hellenic peoples still preserved the traces of this cataclysm, long, long after they could associate it with any particular place or a date. Even now, we can only speculate about the nature of this historical trauma, piecing together the facts of geography and the fragments of legend.

Once upon a time (the traditional story ran) a fortunate race of men inhabited the most beautiful of all islands. In form it was almost perfectly circular, so that men knew it as Strongyle (the Round One): it rose up gently from the seashore to a domed peak, then sloped down to the sea again on the other side. It was a green island with a wonderful climate: thermal springs and perpetual sunshine co-operated to yield perfect harvests in half the usual time. The very soil itself seemed to be blessed by the Gods with a fruitful warmth beyond that of other lands. No wonder the inhabitants counted themselves particularly fortunate, calling their island not just Strongyle but also Kalliste – the Most-Beautiful. Others again called the island Atlantis. It lay near to the Pillars of Hercules, the last headlands of the navigable sea, which served as the last visible landmarks before one reached out into the limitless ocean.

Then one day (the story went on) Poseidon rose up in anger. All round the shores of the Hellas, the waters broke over the land, bringing death and devastation; and, when men returned to where Strongyle had been, they found that it had been engulfed. The fertile green dome had vanished. Charred and stained in lurid patterns of red and black, uninhabitable and uninhabited, nothing remained of that Fortunate Island but a few miles of smoking rim – otherwise, the sea had swallowed it up, along with all its inhabitants. The horrified visitors shielded their nostrils against the Fumes of the Underworld, turned their boats, and fled back to their own lands as fast as they could go. From that time on, men steered clear of Strongyle, and the memory of its former blessed state eventually faded from their minds. From generation to generation, men passed on to their children and grandchildren only the bare legend of a blessed land at the very limits of navigation, which was finally engulfed by the ocean. As time went on, they themselves learnt to navigate further afield, and the legend travelled with them; until at last, having passed beyond Sicily and Sardinia to the point where Spain meets Africa in a new pair of 'Pillars of Hercules', they looked out on the unbounded ocean beyond, and asked themselves what lands it might contain. And then the story of Altantis came back to their minds, and they christened that furthest sea the 'Atlantic'. . . .

So much we can reconstruct from legend. History has only a few quanta to contribute to this intellectual reconstruction. In A.D. 1657, for instance, a French Jesuit called Father Richard wrote his own *Relation de l'Isle de Sant-Erini*. Santorini, he said, was also known as Devil's Island, for the very good reason that it had come from the Nether Regions. In the middle of its central lagoon there were two barren islands called the Burnt Islands: the smaller of these had appeared above water as recently as 1573, while the larger had been formed by three successive eruptions, in the years 12, 726 and 1427. Father Richard himself had visited the island shortly after a renewed series of earthquakes (notably those of 1650 and 1655), which had given rise to tidal waves in the vicinity. Beyond this, he has little to tell us: the impulse to moralize overcomes him, and for most of his *Relation* he is denouncing the island's inhabitants and all their works. The eruptions, in his opinion, were quite simply the fully-merited Wages of Sin, and people in other countries should take heed of the example offered by the island, to reform themselves before the Ever-Loving God subjected them, too, in His Infinite Justice and Mercy, to the well-deserved fate of Sodom and Gomorrah....

Geography has its own story to tell, based on the events of 1883. In that year the island of Krakatau, between Java and Sumatra, blew its top off. The violence of the resulting cataclysm exceeded anything which nuclear technology, even at its most monstrous, has yet achieved. The sound of the eruption was heard 2,000 miles away, and all over the world seismographs recorded as many as half-a-dozen successive jerks, as the shock-wave travelled round and round the Earth. Near the island, the blast-wave was of great force, breaking windows over a radius of 100 miles. On Krakatau itself, no life survived, while the neigh-bouring coast of Java was devastated. The worst damage was done by a tidal-wave – or more properly a *tsunami*, since 'tides', of course, have nothing to do with the case. This broke over Java with a height of ninety feet, and swept inland for several miles. (Even 1,000 yards inland, the wave was still forty-five feet high.) Ships and locomotives were tossed around like pebbles, and 35,000 people were killed, most of them instantly. What the water left undone, fire completed. The cataclysm struck at night, and thousands of oil-lamps thrown over by the blast ignited a line of fires along the fringe of the more immediate devastation.

Now geographers tell us that the island of Santorini shows every sign of having 'blown its top' at some time in the past, in exactly the same way as Krakatau. The phenomenon is, in fact, well-known to volcanologists: it can occur at any point along the volcanic faults in the Earth's crust. Local pressures, building up below a weak spot, first throw up a domed crust; and, later on, this explodes with great violence before collapsing inwards to leave only the rim of a volcanic crater. Between the *cratera* of Krakatau and that of Santorini, there are only two significant differences. First the explosion of Krakatau is a matter of recent history, whereas that of Santorini took place (according to the indications) within a century or so either side of 1400 B.C.; and, secondly, the area of the crater at Santorini is nearly *four times* that of Krakatau. Both eruptions took place in volcanic islands. If the cataclysm of Krakatau produced a destructive *tsunami*, so also (presumably) must that of Santorini: triggered off by an initial eruption several times larger, and travelling over the shallower waters of the Mediterranean, this would have been even higher than the Javanese *tsunami* of 1883. At a distance of 100 miles, its height must still have been anything up to a 150 feet: all round the Aegean, it must have struck the sea-coasts with enough force to do serious damage, while Crete – a mere seventy-five miles away across the open sea – was exposed to the worst of its violence. Since the most prosperous cities of the Minoan Kingdom were the coastal towns along the northern shore, this blow would have fallen from the worst possible quarter, and was capable of disrupting the social life of the island – for the time being, at any rate – almost completely.

At the crucial points, however, history and archaeology remain tantalizingly silent. We can be certain that the eruption took place: that it was at least as severe as the Krakatau disaster; and that its date – within 100 years or so – was 1400 B.C. As for the resulting *tsunami*: if we take into account the layout of the Aegean, its characteristics can reasonably be inferred. Yet, however far back we press the frontiers of history, the eruption remains in the realm of legend: the world of Atlantis, Strongyle and the Deluge of Deukalion.

From Minoan Crete itself, no chronicles survive. Archaeologists (it is true) have seen evidence of a sudden political weakening sometime in the years between 1500 and 1200 B.C., when several of the northern towns appear to have been destroyed by fire; yet they have usually put this destruction down to an attack by political rivals from overseas. Curiously enough, the towns were rebuilt after the disaster without any fortifications, and in some cases on top of ruins filled with masses of seasand. So the possibility remains open – though unconfirmed – that the terrors which struck down Minoan Crete about 1400 B.C. had the same natural cause as the devastation which laid waste western Java in 1883: first a deafening blast-wave, cracking walls, blowing open doors and windows, extinguishing some lamps and upsetting others, so that the towns were filled with fire and darkness; and after it a gigantic wave of water, bearing down on the island from the North, engulfing all the ships in its path, and storming against the coast, to overwhelm the stricken cities and surge inland, destroying farms and crops as far as the very foothills of the mountains. In a harsh, all-too-literal sense of the phrase, the Minoans 'would not know what had hit them'.

*   *   *

Even today, 3,300 years later, Santorini still has the look of a town clearing up after an air-raid – an appearance which it owes only marginally to the most recent earthquake, in 1956. Just west of the north-south diameter, the rim of the circular crater is broken in two places, on both the northern and the southern sectors. We motored in through the northern entrance late in the afternoon, having spent a long grey day making the trip across from Sifnos. Great streaks of red oxide smudged the rocky cliffs at the entrance, and the white houses of Oia clung perilously to the edge of the rim, some 800 feet above us. They looked like doll's houses on the rim of a blast furnace. Ahead of us, the inner coastline of the island unfolded itself, for the most part either sheer cliff or near-vertical pumice scree. The whole barren ochreous wall encircled a lagoon six miles across and 1,200 feet deep, while ahead of us, in the centre, we could now see quite clearly the black humps of those natural slag-heaps, the Burnt Islands. Inquisitive rather than attracted, we rounded a last headland and tied up at the port. There was the usual handful of customs and harbour officials, two or three sailors in a café, but otherwise no sign of life. Immediately above us, a zig-zag wall showed how the cliff-track clambered through the dusk 600 feet and more up to the cliff-hanging houses of the town. Night fell: the last pale gleam from the whitewashed buildings looking down over the lip of the crater faded into the dark, and gave way to a necklace of lights strung across the sky below the stars.

By day, the bomb-damaged appearance of the island was, if anything, reinforced. After a few hours, our noses became inured to the volcanic vapours that drifted across from the simmering vent of the central slag-heap (for the craters on the Burnt Islands are still periodically active). Yet there remained something demoniac, something infernal about the island; for the harshness of Nature leaves the inhabitants with the bare choice between extremes of poverty and rapacity. Light had scarcely returned before the whole quayside was filled with a confused din – the braying of mules mixed with human shouts of 'Elax! Elax!' – and a crowd of muleteers gathered like hornets around anyone who set foot ashore. Two or three times a day during our visit, cargoes of sightseers from cruise-ships were discharged onto the wharf, and for some minutes there would be pandemonium (*sfff*); after which (*molto con brio*) the saddle-sore mules were prodded (*accelerando ma no troppo*) and exhorted ('Elax! Elax!') into carting another load of customers up to the waiting shop-keepers above; after which (*sempre decrescendo*) peace would temporarily return. Meanwhile, in the little town itself, the scar-tissue had grown thick.

Yet, since the destruction of Kalliste, what else is left for the human race to do here? The very beauty of the climate is now an obstacle, since the scanty rainfall, painfully collected in tanks, is too small to sustain rich crops on the thin volcanic soil. (In the town, the only effective gardening is done on the roofs of the houses.) As for industry: that means one thing alone – pumice, parched and angular, fragments picked from the island's crumbled skeleton. The porous rock is quarried out of the hillside, loaded onto a lorry and tipped over the edge of the crater, to cascade down a long scree into the waiting hoppers below, so providing work for perhaps a dozen men. A few tomatoes, a few vines and the natural possibilities of the island are exhausted. All that remains is tourism. . . .

This paradox remained as the most enduring memory of our visit to Santorini. On the one hand, there was the seeming kindliness of Nature: blue sky dotted with white clouds, fields rising gently from the outer shore towards the vanished summit, in some places petering out into dry sand at the foot of palm-trees, but elsewhere continuing smoothly right to the very cliff edge. On the other hand, there was the barren brutality of that same Nature – the 'harsh nurse' of Leopardi's poem *The Broom*:

> . . . vegga quanto
> il gener nostro in cura
> all'amante natura. E la possanza
> qui con giusta misura
> anco estimar potrà dell'uman seme,
> cui la dura nutrice, ov'ei men teme,
> con lieve moto in un momento annulla
> in parte, e può con moti
> poco men lievi ancor subitamente
> annichilare in tutto.

> . . . gaze and see
> how loving Nature cares
> for our poor human race, and learn to value
> at a just estimate the strength of Man
> whom the harsh nurse, even when he fears it least,
> with a slight motion does in part destroy,
> and may, with one scarce less
> slight than the last, without a moment's warning
> wholly annihilate.

On the slopes of such a volcano, as Leopardi cheerlessly insisted, optimism is irrelevant. One lives from year to year. On the Burnt Islands, indeed, one does not – cannot – live at all. Two small coves intersect the largest slag-heap, and provide the boatmen with shelter from the north-west gales. From one of these a track leads over to the principal volcanic vent: one scrambles first up a vertical 'stye' from the dolls'-chapel by the cove onto the dusty crest of the heap, then tramps for three-quarters of a mile across the crunching surface of the dome to the actual crater. Here, in a depression some thirty feet deep, glinting yellow streaks of crystalline sulphur surround the apertures from which the white subterraneous fumes emerge. In places, the slag-pile has begun to cover itself with rough grass, where wind-borne seeds have lodged themselves for long enough to germinate; but, all along an abrupt line, this tentative green is cut short and replaced by sheer black, where a more recent upheaval from below keeps on record Nature's power 'con moti poco men lievi . . . annichilare in tutto'.

Yet humanity clings to life on Santorini, with the same tenacity as the golden broom on Leopardi's Vesuvius. Across on the far side of the island the monastery church, ruined in the most recent earthquake, is in course of being rebuilt: under its shadow, an old lady is content to live in poverty, with a small puppy for company. Halfway over the island in another direction, a small village is preparing for Easter: in the enclosed courtyards of the houses, women and children are rolling, cutting and baking the traditional shortbread biscuits. But poverty is not always bearable – for the fisherman's family out of luck, for the pumice-quarriers threatened with silicosis, for the blind and the lonely. As always in Greece, dignity has the power of steel; but even steel can be strained to cracking-point. Here in Santorini, the first step to prosperity is the price of a mule, and a well-placed café can make your fortune. (Pressed past refusal to sign the visitors' book, Maureen leaves her parting message – 'What a Shark!') By the end of twenty-four hours, our own responses are becoming cynical. Even generosity seems to reflect – in David Hume's unforgettable phrase – 'a lively sense of favours to come'. Tom and Maureen pay a state visit to the Mayor, who speaks very scornfully about the café-proprietor. Next morning a present of the Mayor's own wine arrives accompanied by a glowing message, inviting Maureen to repeat the visit. We uncork the bottle. The Mayor's wine has the *bouquet* of paint-remover, but not (alas) the efficacy.

On the map, the surviving antiquities of Santorini appeared to be easily accessible; to round off our visit we set out for them, cameras and all, in the single serviceable taxi. Having got there, we found that we were faced with a 1,200 foot peak, which could be reached only from a narrow col, high above the sea. The beginnings of a road wound to and fro up the hillside towards this col, only to give out half-way, where a team of soldiers was still at work upon it. We left the taxi, unloaded the very minimum of equipment, and climbed the rest of the way on foot. As we crested the col, we lost the last shelter: the sharp mountain ridge was whipped by a cutting northerly wind from under the low cloud. A more desolate and unpromising site for a city could scarcely be chosen: its sole merit was defensibility. Among the low scrub, nothing remained but a jumble of stones. A few elegant inscriptions caught our eyes, but like nearly everything else there, they dated from 300 B.C. or later. (A few antediluvian remains, dating from perhaps 1800 B.C., were excavated some years ago on the other half of the island, but shortly after being unearthed they were buried again by a further eruption.) The guardian of the site had no set piece to offer us – nothing to compare with the dramatic recitation we had been given in Agamemnon's palace at Mycenae. What we had really come to see, he took it for granted, was the local obscenity: the phallus carved in bas-relief on the wall of the 'House of the Friends'. So he kept trying to shake off June and Helen, in order to show the men of the party where this unique attraction could be found. After a while, he gave up trying to entertain us, and we gave up hope of finding anything worth filming. Chilled, irked, and at a loss, we stood shivering in the little Roman theatre. Tempers cracked. For the first and last time on the expedition, our group was split apart by an open quarrel. The malaise of the island was infecting us. It was time to go, before any more damage was done.

*　　*　　*

'Notice ingenious wave-design of Floor, also Painting mit Dolphins und other Fisches schwimmings.' We had spent Good

Friday corkscrewing our way across the Sea of Crete to Heraklion, and were celebrating our return to dry land by a visit to Knossos. Turning a corner in the ruins, we chanced on a conducted tour, to which the wonders of Minoan civilization were being explained in general-purpose Middle Low Anglo-German. We gazed dutifully at the floor: this appeared to us to be wavy, not by design, but merely through the effects of use and the efflux of time. 'Also very interesting to see,' the guide continued coyly, 'is Queen's Toilet-Room. Notice Clay-Pipes, mit wasser always coming down. Also cover to keep aus Schmell – very modern Systeme.' We squeezed our way past the attentive party and out into the open courtyard. A long passage led to the roofless storerooms, in which stood Ali Baba jars like those we had seen at Sifnos: here, at any rate, one could feel some living contact between the past and the present. In other respects, Knossos was dumb. The glaring frescoes redecorating the walls of the ruins – the Bull, the Lilies, the Dolphins – had the offensive incongruity of rouge and lipstick on a woman of ninety. Even the symbolic bull's-horns, carefully restored and reinstated at the South end of the site, had the air of some architectural fancy by Basil Spence.

True: we were in a jaundiced mood. The sixteen-hour crossing from Santorini had been arduous to live through. Designed to serve as a Norwegian lifeboat, the *Jack London* was guaranteed not to sink; but, short of that, she did almost everything else. All morning we had had the north-westerly *meltem* blowing on the starboard quarter, and after it had dropped, about midday, a steep sea continued to run from the same direction throughout the afternoon. Our bearing for Heraklion being due South, the *J. L.* had surged along her course with a lurching yaw of peculiar sickeningness, and though the topmost peaks of Mount Ida came in sight towards the end of the afternoon, it was ten o'clock at night before we were safely tied up in the little Venetian inner-harbour.

We had filming to do in the museum at Heraklion, and this could not be done before Monday at the earliest; so we had the Easter week-end ahead of us. But the miasma of Santorini was slow to clear. With nine people living on the boat designed to sleep four, we were beginning to irritate one another. Ashore in Crete, the ship's complement exploded in every direction. I myself have confused memories of Saturday evening spent in the streets of Heraklion – crowds jamming the square round the Morosini fountain, to catch a glimpse of the candle-light procession, with its ikons, incense and sacred relics. These jostle with other memories of Easter Day afternoon spent in the local barracks, where the Greek Army was 'At Home' to the general public – crammed at wooden benches and machine-gunned with conversational gambits by enthusiastic cadets from Missolonghi, Mytilene, Athens and Thessalonika. June and I were stuffed with cold lamb and fruit and retsina, until we cried off in exhaustion. Tom Crichton had come with us and was just beginning to enjoy himself. He exhorted us not to give offence by being 'bad guests', but we could not keep it up and excused ourselves, so giving offence – oh dear – to *him*.

Monday's images: the town filled with dust and sand from a *sirocco*, the wind dry on the tongue and the dust-storm tasting as though it had come straight from the Sahara. We try filming indoors, but have trouble with the lights and are short of a backcloth. Following a trail step by step across the town, Robbie and I at last discover a draper's shop. ('Keep asking,' he quotes the Greek proverb – 'and you'll get to Constantinople in the end.') The shop-keeper's wife is at home upstairs and urges us in. Half-an-hour of conversation; cognac and little cakes; tales of the war-time Resistance, and of smuggling British escapees out of the town, disguised as peasant crones and hunchbacks. I lift my glass of liqueur to her –

'This is really extremely kind of you,' I say.

'Not at all,' she answers: 'It is a holiday, and besides – we are humans.'

The draper returns. He is delighted to show us his stock, and we choose a deep-red velvet. We only want two metres – 'What does that matter?' He reaches down a pair of shears and spits quietly. Applying the shears to the edge of the cloth, he murmurs to himself before cutting: 'May it turn out well.' His words ring a bell in my mind: yes, that is it – we are nearing the boundary between Christendom and Islam.

⋆ ⋆ ⋆

The spell which Santorini had laid upon us was finally lifted on the Wednesday. This happened quite suddenly, during a bus-journey from Heraklion to Sitia, at the eastern end of Crete. After finishing our museum-work on the Tuesday, three of us chose to do the next leg of the journey overland, so as to see a little more of the island before we rejoined the *Jack London* for the next lap, across the sea to the Dodecanese. That was how we came to be rattling along, over an unpaved mountain road, in that shuddering bone-shaker of a bus.

For the first thirty miles out of Heraklion, the journey was comparatively civilized. The vehicle reminded me (it is true) of a vintage omnibus I had experienced in Majorca, whose ceiling had been decorated with encrusted wallpaper; but, however rough, the Cretan conveyance was fast and powerful and, initially at any rate, the road was surfaced. We ran through fields of early corn, with wild purple gladioli waving among the green, past Chersonisos (where we caught a glimpse of the *J. L.* chugging along half-a-mile off-shore) to the little town and banana plantations of Malia. A short distance further on, the road turned abruptly inland: the bus pulled up beside a chapel and the passengers all hurried to dismount. The next stretch of road, we were told, was tricky and dangerous. No one could set off across the mountain to Neapolis and Ayios Nikolaos unless he had first interceded with St George for a safe passage. We took the hint, squeezed one way into the crowded chapel and bought our candles.

Two minutes later we were off again. All the way from Hera-klion the loudspeaker above the driver's seat had been filling the bus with the rattle of *bouzouki* music. Now the driver turned the volume up still further, to distract us from the hazards of the journey. We climbed through a fierce grey gorge onto an ele-vated plateau, and clattered into Neapolis in the middle of the

116

morning. Here we were made to change buses: all the luggage was handed from roof-rack to roof-rack, and we settled down again in an even more ancient conveyance. We came down to the sea again at Ayios Nikolaos and stopped for half-an-hour. Setting off again, we at once left the paved road for a cross-country track: ahead of us the last bastions of eastern Crete swung round in an arc beyond the Gulf of Merabellos.

The farther we went, the more relaxed the atmosphere in the bus became. Once we had left the tarmac for the more primitive road beyond, things eased up still more. The bus – fortunately for our bones and our goods – went more slowly. Losing some of their anxiety (in Crete a bus-ride is still regarded with some of the terror of an air-flight elsewhere) the passengers began to sing. A talkative man in the back seat popped up and down like a jack-in-the-box, and broke into a flood of oratory. We had – as it were – changed from the impersonality of an express-train to the more casual friendliness of a cross-country branch line.

At first we skirted the gulf, crossing behind the marshy estuaries of several small rivers. From one of the coastal pools, we put up a heron; in another, an egret stood calm, white and immobile, as we went by. Ten miles on, and we were climbing into the mountains again, the iron cliffs and headlands leaving no space for a road along the coast. Up and up we climbed, with all the serpentine meandering of a road in the Balkans. At one moment, we would sight a village across a valley, and decide that it must be off our route; but no, after driving away from it for a quarter of an hour, we would wind our way round the head of several streams and burst into it from the rear – thereafter hairpinning back and stalking the next village in the same roundabout way. And it was while the bus was resting for its regulation ten minutes, after taking one of its victims by surprise, that I spotted that headline. In front of me, a countryman was reading the front page of his paper with close attention –

Ο ΠΡΩΤΟΣ ΚΟΣΜΟΝΑΥΤΗΣ ΣΤΟ ΔΙΑΣΤΗΜΑ

I sat up and looked again. '*O protos Kosmonautes sto diastema . . .* The first cosmonaut in . . .' – that last word must mean 'Space'.

A man in space, indeed? Message datelined 'Moscow', too! I jogged June's elbow. But, before I could draw her attention to the headline, the diesel engine burst once more into vibrant life. Shuddering and rattling, our spacecraft got under way again, winding through the last of the mountains that separated us from Sitia. This was no longer the time or the place to be reading your neighbour's newspaper. A few miles further on we crossed a col, and came within range of the local radio station. Once again the driver switched on his set, and the loudspeaker filled the bus with music. Freewheeling down the last foothills, we made a successful re-entry into the coastal plain, and came to a stop in the little seaport about half-past four in the afternoon; and two hours later, after an easy passage, the *Jack London* turned up in the harbour also.

I shall always be glad to have heard about Gagarin's space flight in the way we did. If we had been in any big modern city – Athens, as much as London or New York – we should have been in danger of being 'bulldozed by clamour'. As it was, nothing could destroy our sense of proportion, or deceive us into think-ing that space-technology was anything but monumentally irrelevant to the basic problems of twentieth-century human life. Here in Eastern Crete, daily existence leaves room only for essentials. The outdoor cinema comes one day a week, and on the quayside a temporary booth conceals the 'Amazing Spectacle' of a professional Fat Woman. (Robbie pays his entry fee, takes a quiz inside, and comes out again: 'Eight months pregnant,' he declares with a cynical grin.) Otherwise life depends on one's skill at spearing octopuses, loading coastal steamers, or using one's traditional tools to cultivate the narrow plain which here inter-venes between the mountains and the sea. And what will a Man on the Moon do for the fishermen, sailors and farmers of Sitia?

Our first plan was to stay in the port only for one night, and then make due East round the Iron Cape, and so to Carpathos and Rhodes. This plan now miscarried. Two mornings in succession we got up and made ready to leave, only to find that the *meltem* outside the harbour was blowing too hard for comfort. Rather than waste these days, we enrolled help from among the local fishermen and got on with our filming. Our chief recruit was a young fisherman with the clean-cut looks and light hair of a Lombard, and the name – Ah, the Glory that was Venice! – of Manoli Mastropavlis. We were suffering, he told us, from a premature summer wind: a *proi meltem*, as he called it. In this weather, we should have to leave harbour either late at night, or just before dawn (*proi, proi*) – 'when the sea turns to yoghourt'. Meanwhile, he would take us across the bay in a motor-boat, to carry on with our work on the fine sandy beach which lay the other side.

We piled in, cameras and all, and swept across to the far shore on the crests of the rollers. Timing our landing with care, we took turns to jump ashore onto the rocks, and hauled the equipment over a headland to a small farmhouse beside the head of the beach. Behind the house, there was a small paved terrace, overhung by a vine which was just bursting into leaf; and beyond, across a dusty track, was an acre or two of careful tilth, won back by time and labour from the surrounding bamboos. Careful rows were laid out economically across it: beans, tomatoes, peppers, corn – the staples of Mediterranean country life.

'Come inside.' Manoli waved us in at the door, and introduced us to the occupants. The matriarch received us gravely, and set her daughter-in-law – who was, in truth, eight months pregnant – to the task of preparing coffee. The interior of the house comprised simply a rectangular floor of beaten earth, on which stood a small rush mat and four or five upright wooden chairs. Above the black charcoal stove in one corner, there were sacred pictures cut out of coloured magazines. Over the single small window and the open door hung curtains of plain sacking.

Two small boys entered and stood by our chairs, gazing at us with an utterly unmalicious curiosity. Their hair was shaved almost to the scalp, and eyes of the most intense blue stared silently at us as we talked. A small white dog came in with them, looking as closely shaved as themselves. (How would a Tibetan Spaniel get to Crete?) A couple of minutes later, the farmer himself came in, stamping and brushing the dust of the fields from off his hands. Introductions were repeated, and the ceremonies of hospitality went on: since there were only three *demi-tasses* to drink from, the women of the house were kept busy, preparing several brews of coffee in succession. This time at any rate we were determined not to be 'bad guests', so we sat quietly, taking our turns and joining in the conversation as best we could. Soon Manoli, Fotis and the farmer were engrossed in a discussion of the latest news. After an orbit in space, the Moon; after the Moon (they supposed) then presumably Venus or Mars. . . . It was a noteworthy feat, they agreed – content, apparently, that the scope of man's achievement should widen in this way, despite all their own poverty and needs.

So we all sat, coming to terms, in our different ways and against our different backgrounds, with this latest fulfilment of the modern mechanical vision of Nature. Meanwhile, everything around us fell naturally into the alternative patterns that had moulded the older organic view. The world of mechanisms had not (it was clear) displaced the organic world: it had merely overlaid it. And here, at any rate, the two worlds, old and new – Ancient and Modern – could co-exist peacefully and without problems.

7 · A passage to Asia

The focus of our problems now shifted. We were well started on one half of our inquiries, but it was time to ask some fresh questions. For, though we had apparently got a little way into the minds of the first natural philosophers, and recognized for ourselves some of the things that served as starting-points for their speculations, this helped us to understand only the *content* of their theories. It left quite unanswered another group of questions: namely, those about the *conditions* which made possible that first germination of rational thought about Nature. (If the Renaissance of science and learning, from A.D. 1450 on, is an historical phenomenon whose very occurrence is a challenge to the historian's understanding, how much more of a challenge is this original Naissance of philosophy and science 600 years before Christ.) Why should science and philosophy have been born where they were – in those small Greek communities along the Aegean and Italian coastlines, rather than in (say) the richer and more powerful empires of Mesopotamia and Egypt? And why did this intellectual florescence begin at the time it did – in those particular few hundred years, rather than five or fifty centuries earlier or later?

These, of course, are questions that scholars have argued about long and passionately; and, in thinking about them, it is hard to be sure even that one's questions are framed in the right terms – to say nothing of one's answers being correct. Still: though we were under no illusion that we were going to reach any final answers, there should be some virtue in an on-the-spot inspection of the region where science began. With luck, the clues this would reveal might help us, at least, to see our *questions* in proportion. So, following in the footsteps of Freya Stark, our Quest now took us to Ionia.

In our original plan, we were to strike East from Sitia to Carpathos, and from there north-eastwards to the island of Rhodes, where we were to call first at Lindos, and then at the port of Rhodes itself. For our purposes, Carpathos held out great promise: dry, rugged, off all the main routes, it has preserved intact, more than most of the Aegean islands, the ancient habits of life and modes of dress. Exploring Carpathos in the years 1902–4, Professor Dawkins described the near-Homeric traditions surviving in the northern part of the island. Around the village of Elymbos (or Olympus) the costumes, the songs, and even the building-methods, seemed unchanged from 3,000 years ago. There was, for instance, a special variety of door-lock known as a *mandala*, which worked on the same principles as one described in the Iliad; and in the ravine below Elymbos, he noted – so making our mouths water – there was an old wooden olive-press and mill of quite remarkable design.

Inquiries in Athens reinforced our interest in Carpathos. The M.P. for the Dodecanese Islands told us that most of these archaic customs still survived into the nineteen-sixties. The local women's dress – a long white-sleeved undergarment, covered by a shorter blue-sleeved coat open at the front, with double kerchiefs on the head and full white trousers tied at the ankle – this we should certainly find around Elymbos: once, that is, we had managed the ascent to this little eagle's-nest of a town, perched on a mountain col far above the sea. And, if we could get the villagers of Elymbos to sing for us, we should record folk-music quite unlike anything be heard in other parts of Greece. Fired by these prospects, we had put Carpathos very firmly on our list of islands to visit.

Now it had to come off again. We had lost four days from our schedule, two at Heraklion and two at Sitia. April was already half gone, and we must be in Turkey at the beginning of May. Meanwhile, there was a great deal to be done, notably in Samos, and we could no longer afford any detours. We sat over the Admiralty charts with a pair of dividers, stepping out the distances separating us from Cos, Samos and Kushadasi – the only serious port left today on the Ionian coast. However we planned our route, the conclusion was hard to escape: the distance to Cos alone was 120 miles and, unless the *meltem* disappeared, any of the laps from Crete to Cos and Calymnos, Patmos, Samos and beyond, might prove tricky. Regretfully we struck Carpathos and Rhodes off the list, and decided on an early start for Cos.

The revised plan had one incidental advantage: we should be following the route of history. The first birthplace of science was Miletus, which in 600 B.C. was a flourishing port at the mouth of the Greater Meander, not far south of Samos. There the first recorded school of 'natural philosophers' thought and argued: Thales, its founder, being followed by Anaximander and Anaximenes. By their time, the city had been a flourishing port for several hundred years: it certainly existed in the eleventh century B.C., and Homer refers to Carians from Miletus as having fought on the Trojan side against Agamemnon and the Greeks from the mainland. (Many of the 'Trojans' in the *Iliad* were, of course, what we should call Asiatic Greeks.) But where did the first Greek-speaking colonists of Miletus come from themselves? Though this question is still wrapped in a historical fog, the little evidence we have points in a plausible direction: several of the Greek names associated with Miletus have been found also in Crete – the name 'Thales' is itself one of these. And since, around 1500 B.C., the main foci of power in the Greek world lay in the Peloponnese and in Minoan Crete, the supposition that Ionia was colonized from Crete is, historically speaking, quite possible.

Technically speaking, too, this was also quite a possible route. During the second millennium B.C., after having reached the Mediterranean from their earlier homes in the interior of Asia, the Greek tribes were gradually accustoming themselves to a life lived beside the sea, on it and from it. Lacking the compass, the stern-post rudder, and all those other devices by which modern navigation has become so much more certain an art, the first Aegean sailors were never able to tackle the open ocean. They began by coast-hopping, and went on – more daringly – to island-hopping; but either way they took good care not to go out of sight of land. In good weather, they could thus rely on finding their way from point to point. But once caught by a storm in the dark and thrown off course, they were exposed to all the terrors and unknowns of the *Odyssey*.

By the direct route, then, Sitia to Cos is some 120 miles; but they are not miles of absolutely empty sea. For most of the first 100 miles, it is true, there are no regularly-inhabited islands – these begin only when one reaches the line of the Dodecanese, which stretches north-west from Rhodes, through Nisiros and Cos, as far as Patmos. Still, dotted across the eastern end of the Sea of Crete which lay ahead of us, there were ten or a dozen barren islets, which would serve us as milestones along the way. For us, they would be no more than useful confirmation that our own work with the compass, map and rudder had been in order. For the Greeks of 1500 B.C., these rocks and islets were a lifeline, along which – given good weather – they could find their way safely between Crete and Asia Minor.

Our third evening at Sitia, the weather was at last settling down. With this slight improvement, café life along the harbour brightened up. After dinner we sat out on deck: there were stars once again, and lights along the quay, and music from loudspeakers propped above the doors of the bars. We remembered Manoli's advice to leave *proi, proi*. Like all sea-breezes, the *meltem* gets up with the sun and freshens as the day goes on, slackening again at sunset. So our plan was to get clear away from the dangers of the coast in the early hours, and to carry the wind all day for as far as we could, shortening sail if need be. By four in the morning, Tom and Maureen were up and casting off from the jetty. When I came on deck a few minutes later, the red harbour-light was falling astern, and the bows were beginning to throw out, first necklaces, next waves, and finally whole sheets of phosphorescence, as they dipped and rose on meeting the first of the swell outside. We made course north-easterly out of the Bay of Sitia, to pass under the lee of the two Yianisadhes Islands (also known – like so many Mediterranean rocks – by the name of Dragonada). Soon there was a steady sailing-breeze, and the heavy boat began to push along at five knots. The last rugged promontory of north-eastern Crete (*Akro Sidheros*, the Iron Cape) fell gradually away to starboard, and beyond it 'rosy-fingered dawn' brought life and colour back to the 'wine-dark sea'. This would be the longest single lap of our journey, and we savoured its Homeric flavour.

As the day brightened and we reached further out to sea, so the *meltem* freshened. With it there came a deepening beam swell, which marched down from the central Aegean to our left, and on past us towards Carpathos and the Eastern Mediterranean. With both wind and sea just abaft the beam, the *Jack London* rolled heavily, and before long everyone was up on deck. June and Helen kept cheerful for a few minutes, but succumbed in the end, curling up under rugs in sheltered corners of the deck, where they lay, a silent and angular cargo, facing the prospect of twenty-four hours' purgatory. Before long they were beyond the power of Dramamine or anything else. For myself, I was better off. On a trip of this kind, one can make as much of a job of navigating as one pleases: taking bearings on each new land-mark as it comes into view, keeping track of one's changing position on the chart, and following one's progress along the chosen route. Before we had finally dropped the Iron Cape out of sight astern, the first rocky milestone was in sight ahead – the un-inhabited twin islands of Unia. Shortly afterwards they were followed by the tiny Egg Rock (*Avga* in Greek) to port, and by Stakida to starboard.

By midday, Stakida was silhouetted against a bunch of cotton-wool clouds which rested, fixed and tantalizing, on the rim of the horizon. Under them, I realized, lay the rocky spine of Carpathos – in places little more than two miles across, yet rising in that short distance to a height of some 2,000 feet. As the shadow of Elymbos slid gently along the horizon, to vanish behind us, I felt some nostalgia for the costumes, the olive-press and the Homeric locks that we should not now see – even more for those stones outside the church, over which (according to Dawkins) the women of the village had inheritable rights, by which only the 'owner' of each stone was entitled to stand on it. Sad to miss those things, I thought; not to mention the archaic folk-music that we were missing the chance to record. . . . And then, of course, there would have been Rhodes. . . .

I turned back to the chart. Our next major landmarks should be the *Tria Nisia* to the south-east of Sirina, but they were still some way ahead. At the moment, we were just about abeam of Sophrano and still going well, tramping through the water at around six knots despite the heavy roll. For an hour or two longer the *meltem* kept up its force, then it began to flag, became fitful, and finally dropped. By the middle of the afternoon we were already losing speed, for the first weakening of the wind left the sea as disturbed as ever: as each wave passed, its crest lifted the *J.L.* by the stern and dropped her labouring into the next trough, so that she lost her earlier power to keep cutting through the swell. By six in the afternoon the sails had effectively ceased to draw. I checked our bearing, and stepped off our progress on the chart with the dividers. We had covered sixty-five of our 120 miles – and that, Tom said, represented as fine a wind and as long a piece of sustained sailing as he had yet had, since he had brought the *J. L.* to the Mediterranean.

'What, only just half-way?' June groaned, and rolled into the scuppers. Tom went below and started up the diesel, while we cleared the sails away. Before long the sun had set, and the quick dusk had begun. From the bows I peered out ahead, hoping to catch a glimpse of the first lights. As the deck rose and dropped on the swell, something glinted ahead, and was lost again behind the waves. We rose, dropped, rose again; and yes, there it was, an unmistakeable light. But *which* light? Was it Kandeliusa, flashing twice every fifteen seconds, or Tilos flashing similarly every sixteen seconds? (Or should Kandeliusa be occulting, instead of flashing? Our two Admiralty charts disagreed.) Probably it was Kandeliusa, which was the nearer of the two lights, and slightly on the port bow: by keeping it to port, we ought by rights to pass between the islands of Tilos and Nisiros; and half-an-hour later this judgment was confirmed when, just to starboard, we picked up the light on Gaidharos (Donkey Island) off the northern point of Tilos.

Now that it was night, June decided that she would be no more miserable down in the cabin than she already was on deck. When the invalids were settled below, I brought my own rugs up and lay in the dark under the stars. The *meltem* had blown the sky brilliantly clear, so that the patterns of the stars shouted at us out of the night. My thoughts soon became incoherent: 'the stars . . . the sailors' friends . . . pity not to get to Rhodes . . . constellations . . . Sirius at Rhodes and at Alexandria. . . .'

*   *   *

I woke rather after midnight, conscious of a change in the boat's motion. Away to the left, the stars were blotted out by a dark shadow. We were rounding Nisiros. The *Jack London* was now heading round towards the North and taking the sea more on her bow, as she made for the straits between Cos and the Turkish mainland. Soon a bright light appeared on the starboard bow, a double white flash every five seconds. We were in sight of Asia.

I sat up and looked around. The upper side of the sleeping-bag was wet under my hand, for there had been a heavy dew: now there was a little spray on the wind as well, from squally gusts coming round the north side of the island. I moved nearer the cockpit, where Fotis and Maureen were sharing the dawn watch. Maureen, at the tiller, was encased as usual in a thick stratum of sailing-jerseys: Fotis (a landsman by upbringing, now taking his first extended yacht-trip) was crouched down in a professional-looking monkey-jacket, with the peak of his cap pulled over his eyes. His transistor radio appeared to be out of order. He fiddled with it for a few minutes, then put it aside and lit a cigarette.

I pointed over towards the flashing light on the Asian shore: 'Cnidus' I said.

'*Legete?*' The name had blown away on the wind, so I leant nearer and repeated it.

'*Kneitus?*' he queried again: then, 'Ah! *Kneethos* . . .', he countered. His face rose like the Moon out of the collar of his jacket and turned towards the shore, broadening into a grin as he associated: '*Kneethos – Nai nai: Efthoxos.*'

We had made our landfall – almost too neatly – at the birthplace of Eudoxus, the first real mathematical physicist. Twenty miles north of Rhodes, an outlying bastion of Asia Minor narrows to an isthmus less than a mile wide. Westward from this Dorian isthmus runs a mountainous promontory some thirty miles long, which reaches a height of nearly 4,000 feet before plunging into the Aegean at the ancient Cape Triopium. Today the Dorian Promontory lies, sleeping and forgotten, at the south-western extremity of modern Turkey: for those wishing to travel along it, the *Guide Bleu* foresees nothing better than a 'very poor track'. But in earlier times, when the whole Hellenic world was bound together as much by a network of sea-highways as by roads overland, this was one of the foci of the world. Just as Miletus and its fellow-cities of the Ionian confederation, further North, shared a communal shrine at Panionium on the mainland shore just to the East of Samos, so the Dorian cities around Cos built their collective shrine on Cape Triopium, alongside the city of Cnidus. Dorian sailors and traders were the Portuguese of the ancient world, pioneering the sea routes to the South and West and setting up trading posts as far away as Sicily and Egypt. For two centuries their chief rivals were the Semitic Phoenicians (who were – so to speak – the Arab navigators of their age) but, as with the Portuguese 2,000 years later, their early achievements were soon overtaken by Greeks from other cities. Living on an island so close to the shore of Asia that the two are now joined by an isthmus, the men of Cnidus were exposed to pressure from the East. The arrival of the Persian armies under Cyrus the Great caught them unprepared. They set about cutting off the whole of their thirty-mile promontory, by digging a canal across its narrow neck; but it was too late. They were over-run, and the city surrendered in 546 B.C.

Cnidus was not finished; but – inevitably – it became more and more of a pawn in the three-cornered struggle between Athenians, Spartans and Persians. For much of the fourth century B.C. it was, in effect, an Athenian dependency: still, though dependent, it remained distinguished and prosperous, being a kind of latter-day Venice of the Ancient era. In the middle of the fourth century the city was still rich enough to commission a highly-adorned statue of Venus from the sculptor Praxiteles, and from Cnidus there came also one of the outstanding mathematicians of Plato's time – Eudoxus.

By 400 B.C., the story of Greek science was some two centuries old, and its intellectual foundations had been firmly established. In outline at any rate, the natural philosophers had built up a first picture of the structure and lay-out of the cosmos. By now, Anaxagoras' explanation of the cause of eclipses was accepted as a commonplace; and the Greeks appreciated equally the distinction between the stars forming the fixed constellations (which swing across above men's heads in unchanging patterns and at a constant rate), and the smaller number of 'wandering' stars or 'planets', which move against this background in a more irregular way. On the theoretical side of science, too, they were well-launched on the development of geometry as a coherent system of mathematical deductions – this was the result of a magnificent piece of co-operative research, and was to culminate, rather over a century later, in the intellectual sky-scraper of Euclid's *Elements*.

The moment seemed ripe for some great stroke of the intellect, which would demonstrate unanswerably the independent power of men's minds. Enough of fact-collecting, said Plato: the time had come to harness men's new, rational understanding of geometry to the well-established observations of planetary motion, and so to frame an intellectual system of a brand-new type – what one might call a *theory* of the heavens. About the general *form* of this novel geometrical picture of the cosmos, Plato was confident enough: we should think of the heavens as built up like a nest of Chinese boxes – a system of spherical shells, which turned within one another about a common centre, each of the planets being carried along its track by one of the concentric spheres. But envisaging the general form of the planetary theory was only a first step: the real master-stroke would be to show, in detail, how such a theory explained the actual wanderings of the planets. For the first time in human history, we meet a group of applied mathematicians faced with a problem in theoretical physics of the most typical sort – namely the problem of envisaging a hypothetical system of relations in Nature, by which the general ideas of their theory could be made to match exactly with the results of observation.

They had one particular key-problem to solve: the so-called 'retrograde motion' of the planets. Whereas the stars march across the vault of the heavens unflaggingly and always in the same direction, the wanderings of the planets are complicated: they not only accelerate and slow down, but at times even turn back across the pattern of the constellations, before resuming their general forward march. The resulting 'loops' in the planetary tracks were the most mysterious problem facing the astronomers of antiquity. How could one reconcile in a common geometrical theory the circular motion of the stars and these complex tracks of the planets? That was the challenge which Heraclides stated, and which Plato propounded to the mathematicians of his time. Of all those who took it up, the one who met it most successfully was Eudoxus. To account for the general forward motion of the planets along the line of the ecliptic, we could assume (he showed) that they were carried by two linked spheres: for the actual loops of the retrogradations, two further, more eccentric spheres were required – turning with opposed motions within the outer pair, these would superimpose a 'horse-fetter', or figure-of-eight, on top of the general advance along the ecliptic. Taken all together, these four superimposed motions yielded a track having all the most striking features of the planets' actual paths. On this geometrical demonstration much of subsequent Greek astronomy was founded – notably, Aristotle's own account of the heavens – and the credit for the discovery belongs to Eudoxus of Cnidus.

The demonstration was, of course, a purely 'academic' exercise. Plato and his fellow-mathematicians were not doing calculations for a living, like the astrological prognosticators of Babylon. Astronomical technology was not their concern: they were obsessed rather by an intellectual possibility – that a novel astronomical science might be constructed on geometrical foundations. By itself, Eudoxus' discovery had no practical application. The Dorian sailors continued to navigate at night by traditional rules-of-thumb inherited from their forefathers: they could learn nothing from the theoreticians of the Academy. Nevertheless, Eudoxus' work was the first major link in a historical chain which led eventually to Newton and the intellectual world of modern science. So far as I was concerned, no place in Asia Minor could have provided a happier landfall.

*　　*　　*

We steered well clear of Triopium: we had been warned beforehand that the Turkish coastguards had little use for strange yachts, and were liable to be trigger-happy. So we kept straight on until, right ahead, we could pick up the light on the southeast corner of Cos, and we left Cnidus for another day. Clearing round the end of the Dorian Promontory, we opened up the Ceramic Gulf, the deep dissected inlet, anything up to fifteen miles wide, which cuts for some fifty miles into the body of south-western Turkey.

By now the stars were fading swiftly and another dawn had begun. Blink-blink: the squally wind had dropped, and the flashing light (blink-blink) on the tip of Triopium was reflected in the calmer waters (blink-blink) at the mouth of the gulf. As the whiter-than-white of a new day began to creep into the sky, both the light and its reflection began to turn yellow. At first, the coast of Asia was no more than a schematic backcloth, coarsely pinked and scalloped out of pitch-black velvet. Devoid of all depth, the line of the peninsula shrank away eastward, to end in the foothills of Anatolia, before swinging back along the northern side of the gulf towards Halicarnassus (the birthplace of Herodotus), which would soon be straight ahead. To our left, the southern face of Cos took on form, if not colour, falling in a single barren sweep from the crest-line of the hills to the shore. In these dawn hours, the sea itself was just as Manoli had described it – a turgid lake stretching away lead-coloured in every direction, with the texture of yoghourt.

Then, as I watched, the daily transformation was swiftly re-enacted. The summit of the mountain closing the head of the gulf suddenly ignited, and by its conflagration (or so it appeared) the sun was reborn. A bell rang in my mind. *That* was what 'Anatolia' meant, of course: 'the sunrise land', or as we should say (substituting Latin for Greek) 'the orient' – the land-mass of Asia Minor, named by the Greeks of the Aegean from their own point of view. In a few minutes, the whole aspect of the scene was changed. The Turkish hills were pried apart by the new-born fingers of light. Spur behind wooded spur, the rugged buttresses of the promontory opened up like pleats, as the first rays brought to life the colour of the trees on their eastward-facing slopes. Across the way, Cos itself changed from pale buff to green; and as we rounded Cape Fourkas for the last coastwise leg to the port of Cos, the curious cone of an island which marks the entrance to Halicarnassus came in sight ahead. We overtook a small lateen-rigged fishing-boat, and rounded the great Crusader castle which guards the entrance to the harbour. By eight o'clock we were tied up, stern to quay – twenty-eight hours out, and a world away, from Sitia.

8 · Samples of the Past

Cos, Patmos, Samos – however one traverses this corner of the Aegean, the stepping-stones on one's route are landmarks, not only in geography, but also in intellectual history. Whatever factors stimulated, or facilitated, or permitted, the unique flowering of free and original thought that took place around this part of the world in the years after 600 B.C., its results were certainly many-sided; and every stage of our journey from Crete to Miletus served to remind us – at the very least – how versatile the classical Greeks were. The different stages also did something to sharpen our problem up for us. For each of the milestones along our way symbolized something rather different. Cos stood for medicine, Patmos for theology, Samos for mathematics and engineering; and only the cities of mainland Ionia – such as Miletus, Ephesus and Clazomenae – for natural science proper.

Why was this? Placed so close together, and having so much else in common, why should these early Greek cities and islands have fostered such contrasted intellectual interests? Did they really differ so much one from another? Or was it only a chance of history that placed an Hippocrates in one city, a Thales in a second, a Pythagoras in a third? Chance, no doubt, played some part in the story; and yet – I suspected – there must be more to it. Even a man of genius cannot create single-handed a whole intellectual tradition. It is not enough that he should be born, live and have ideas. Unless these are discussed, recorded, re-membered; unless he has pupils, successors, or (at the very least) adversaries, no *tradition* will be established, or come down to us. In early times, indeed, his ideas would actually die with him. Being used to the ease with which nowadays, in a free country,

133

one can get one's views and theories printed and published, we tend to think only of the rows of printed books a man leaves behind him as a memorial. Yet books themselves are a modern invention, and books alone do not make an intellectual tradition. The fact remains that in Cos (for example) the ancient intellectual tradition focused on medicine, while on the Ionian mainland it focused on scientific theory, and we must ask why this was so.

As a place, Cos at once beguiled us, and we ended by staying there four days. If we had tried to move on earlier, indeed, June and Helen would have been in a mood to mutiny: after the passage from Crete, their reactions to the prospect of 'a nice sail' were never quite the same. Happily, there was plenty of work to be done at Cos, and in any case the place had a certain air, a charm and ease. . . .

April 16 p.m. June and I wake at half-past-three in the 'Akropol Hotel', a friendly little boarding-house in a shady side street – Wiesbaden architecture again! – back from the waterfront. Afternoon sun falling through the shutters onto our beds. The French windows of our room open onto a balcony, and from this a spiral stair covered with creeper leads up to a flat roof. At last the sun has some warmth in it: we stand on the roof, blinking and stretching, shaking the creases out of our bodies and souls. On this side of the island's rocky backbone, the hills drop gradually to a fertile plain, which stretches away behind the town for as far as we can see. There is a belt of trees along the foot-hills, and somewhere in there (we are told) is the Asclepion, which is our main target.

What really grips us, however, is the view in the other direction. From up here, the harbour forms a triangle of water immediately in front of us, with the great walls of the Crusader castle closing it on the South. Outside the harbour entrance, the sea-channel looks scarcely more than a canal. In fact, a good three miles separate us from the mainland, but the straits are dwarfed by the hilly cape beyond, and the eye is led naturally away from Halicarnassus up to the head of the Ceramic Gulf. Here in the town of Cos, one must always be finding oneself gazing into Asia, and for men whose lives were spent in and out of small boats these Dorian cities – Cos, Cnidus, Halicarnassus and the rest – certainly formed a natural unit. Even today, Athens is fifteen hours away by steamer, Halicarnassus (Bodrum, as the Turks call it) only twenty minutes. We saw, this morning, the small motor-launch that makes the crossing twice daily – not that there is much exchange of goods, still less of people. The disasters of 1922 and 1923 have left too sore a wound. . . .

Later: We have been for a walk through the town. This place is full of the sediment of history – silted up and running over with the relics of all that has happened since classical times. We spent an hour rambling round the castle alone: this was built by the Crusaders and kept intact by the Turks – finally to be transformed, on an instant, from active life into a museum. Laid out now with grass, the courtyards are filled with masonry fragments of every era. Classical and Hellenistic ruins were cannibalized to form the original structure. The Ptolemies of Alexandria, Cleopatra's ancestors, inherited the sovereignty from Alexander the Great and made Cos their favourite summer retreat. (A good choice: the Greek merchants of Alexandria have followed their example ever since.) At the foot of the battlements is a classical bas-relief: a horse carved on the front and a lion behind. Nearby is a row of Crusader coats-of-arms: swastikas, bars-sinister, hatchments, quarterings, supporters. Across the path is a Turkish memorial: the characteristic stylized cypress, with a point like a newly-sharpened pencil, and stone foliage curving delicately inwards to the short, straight trunk. There are even a few relics of the Italian occupation, from 1912 to 1945.

Just outside the castle drawbridge is the great spreading plane-tree known locally as the 'tree of Hippocrates'. Is it really two thousand five hundred years old? Who knows? Once past a certain stage of decrepitude, so that its branches have to be propped on stilts, splinted and supported, a tree becomes ageless. Somewhere hereabouts, at any rate, Hippocrates set up his open-air consulting-room: if one chooses to believe that he sat under this very tree, no harm is done. Vast, leathery, sprawling, with a little stone shrine built into it, it reminds me of some sacred banyan in Ceylon, draped and festooned with prayer lamps.

The presence of Asia is felt everywhere. Under the mosque in the main square is a row of craftsmen's booths and shops. The minaret is trim, and freshly painted. (The catastrophe of 1923 was not absolute, and a thousand Muslims still live and worship here.) As for the thirty Italian years: they have left only a fingerprint – looking into the cemetery behind the town centre, I am transported back by those touching photographs of the dear departed framed into the marble slabs, to its counterpart on Monte Miniato, overlooking Florence.

(Apart from that, the Municipal Buildings, *stilo Mussolini*, are the only obvious reminder.) As so often, it was the earlier generation of Romans whose mark is most unmistakeable. A little way along from the cemetery, an avenue of cypresses leads to their little stone theatre; the usual terraced semi-circle of stone, compact but complete – an antique theatre in a nutshell.

If the Italians clung on to Cos and the other Dodecanese, after taking them from the Turks in 1912, one can hardly blame them. To a far greater extent than any other we had yet visited, this part of Greece has an Italianate air – that *Kennst du das Land* feeling, of lemon-trees under the Riviera sun. This is partly a matter of the climate; for Cos, like Rhodes, basks in the lee of the great Anatolian massif, and this protects it from the local Russian *mistral* in the same way that the Alps protect the stretch of coast between Nice and Sestri Levante. Yet Nature is kind to Cos not only in its weather. Here, the barren ruggedness of the other Greek islands gives way to a fertile plain: not lush, perhaps, but for once generous and adequately watered. If Horace had been a Greek (I thought), he would have got Maecenas to buy him a farm on Rhodes or Cos, for certainly there could be no finer escape from the tensions of city life, and no better place for a rest cure.

A place for a rest cure? Evidently, that is what Hippocrates thought. For Cos is the old original 'watering-place', ante-dating Baden-Baden, Vichy, Tunbridge Wells, Spa and even Bath (for all its Roman origins) by centuries. Most sickness, in Hippocrates' view, had its origin in an unbalanced régime of life: he was the first great exponent of 'environmental medicine'. The foundation of a doctor's wisdom lay in understanding the influences by which his patients were affected – the characters, as he put it, of different 'airs, waters and places'. And those who could not restore a healthy balance in their lives by treatment in their home towns came in large numbers to Cos, seeking cures from the Master himself.

Often enough they were successful. Nobody in need of convalescence after physical strain could fail (we agreed, stretching our muscles and letting our limbs relax) to benefit from a few weeks in this charming place. And for those whose troubles were not purely physical – for the neurotics of the ancient world – Hippocrates and his pupils had a treatment also: their own version of 'incubation'. This practice was, one might say, the first clear forerunner of psycho-analysis, and it started, like Freud's own work, from the interpretation of dreams. It was practised chiefly in the temples of Asclepios, the son of Apollo who was, by tradition, the divine patron of the medical arts. The sick man was placed in the care of a sympathetic priest, given a ritual bath, then put to sleep for the night in the courtyard of the Temple. On waking in the morning, he recounted his dreams to the priest, whose task was to prescribe how the balance of his health should be restored. The success of this treatment depended, no doubt, on the tradition by which the dream-interpretations were guided, and about these, unfortunately, no information has survived. But, during and immediately after Hippocrates' lifetime, the Asclepion at Cos acquired a notable reputation; and of this we have solid evidence – just how solid, we were to see for ourselves the next day.

The island of Cos – in this, too, how unlike most of the Greek islands! – is a land of bicycles. Coming back from our walk round the town, we hired our own, and pedalled out of town as far as the Turkish cemetery which sleeps among the hayfields half-a-mile away. Leaving our bikes against the surrounding wall, we looked inside. There was none of the new-mown finickiness and moral restraint of an English country churchyard, none of that feeling that the dead are still (so to speak) 'in hospital', so needing to have their flowers changed and their sheets straightened and their post-mortal bedpans fetched and carried. The Turkish dead lie easy and undisturbed. Great care is devoted to the headstone – slim, wedge-shaped, frequently capped with a carved turban, the mark of the *hajj* who had made his pilgrimage to Mecca. Apart from that, a square of cypresses is planted around the cemetery, growing almost as trimly and elegantly in Nature as on the stone carvings within the castle at Cos. A surrounding wall completes the design: within it, the grass is left to grow as vigorously as in any field, and only the stone turbans, peering out between the poppies and grasses, show the location of the graves.

Next morning, we rode further out of town, past the little cemetery and on, climbing gradually across the foothills towards the line of woods. As we climbed, the view over the straits continually expanded until, after nearly two miles, we came to an avenue of conifers at the far end of which was an open space at the foot of a great triple terrace. Each level was divided from the one above by a wall of antique masonry, and in the centre of the whole construction the three platforms were linked together by a stone stairway of imposing width.

This, then, was the Asclepion. We dropped our bicycles in the hedge and raced each other up the steps. From the top platform, the view was the best yet. To the left, we could see all along the Turkish coastline northwards, towards Calymnos, Samos and Ionia; Halicarnassus was straight ahead; and beyond it the horizon receded away, to the right, up to the head of the Ceramic Gulf. The main layout of the vast temple-cum-hospital could easily be made out: on the top platform were the foundations of the principal temple, while lower down, with the help of much concrete filling, the Italian authorities had had ineptly reconstructed the columns of a lesser temple. Water still flowed from the two chief mineral springs into stone basins below. Otherwise, the broken pediments and tumbled masonry still lay where they fell in the great earthquake of A.D. 554. June tramped around the platforms, her enthusiasm warming as her directorial eye took in the visual possibilities of the place. Fotis skipped from stone to stone, framing thumbs and forefingers before his eye in an improvised viewfinder, and assembling in imagination beautiful combinations of broken pillars, inscriptions, and wild flowers. For once in a while, his intense feeling for people and their activities – his belief in the power of film as a medium for commenting on social life and problems – was set aside. Finding the artist in him too strong for his own politics, he muttered amused self-reproaches under his breath: 'Dear, oh dear! I *am* being a formalist!'

June was soon clear in her mind that the Asclepion could give her the scene she wanted for drawing her film to a close. The spreading ruins and distant views in combination created the possibility of a striking visual cadence, by which the eye and the mind could be carried away from the details of Greek science to a suitable full-stop. But she needed also a human being to carry (so to say) the melodic line in this cadence, incarnating the powers of the human mind in whose possibilities the Greek scientists had placed their faith. After all: if we had any one thing to learn from them, it was (she insisted) the importance of this self-confidence of the human mind. As Epictetus was later to emphasize, that alone could give a man real protection against irrational fears and superstition: 'Why then do we fear to send a young man out from the schools into life? Knows he not the god within?' And the completed film itself could have a far worse title than *The God Within.*

But there was a problem – how to find someone who could represent Epictetus' 'young man'; and for the next twenty-four hours, as we completed a lot of miscellaneous shooting in and around the harbour and castle, this problem was very much on our minds. Finally we took our courage in both hands, and went to pay courtesy calls on two local dignitaries to whom the M.P. in Athens had given us introductions. The first, a lawyer, was friendly but unhelpful: the second, who sold petrol and fuel-oil on the harbour-front, admitted to having a fine handsome son . . . 'but, alas, he is in Athens!' Shoulders were shrugged, smiles were reciprocated, hands were shaken, and we turned to go. As we left, however, he added, almost parenthetically, 'I have another son.' We turned back sharply. 'Yes, he is here. He is a student. I will send him to see you at seven o'clock.' Wry smiles gave way to broader ones, and smiles themselves to laughter. Firmer handshakes were exchanged, and we went back to the boat more hopefully.

'My son the student' was no Marlon Brando, but (we decided) he would do all right. We gave him his instructions for the next morning, and arranged to set off ourselves at 7.30 a.m. in a hired Chevrolet. The next day was bright and clear: blue and fresh to begin with, bleaching as the hours passed and the heat grew more intense. We went to work with concentration. When Costas Matthaios himself arrived at half-past-eight, tripods and cameras were in place, and detailed shooting was already under discussion. If the young man started sitting on the top step, should he get up and walk straight down the stairway? Or, rather, diagonally across it? And should he . . .? June turned towards her 'star' and stopped. Her jaw dropped. She looked him up and down and turned away, smiling. His hair was kept in place by a glossy layer of brilliantine. On his feet, he was wearing a fashionable pair of suede winkle-picker shoes; and, prominently displayed on his shirt pocket, there was a multi-coloured badge commemorating the Olympic Games of A.D. 1960.

Fortunately, he was not quick to take offence. A pair of nail-scissors detached the offending badge, his fashionable shoes (*ap' ta mytera*) were replaced by my sandals, and by vigorous ruffling the worst of the sheen was soon removed from his hair. June and Fotis returned to their discussions, and the slow business of detailed planning went on. Try it this way, try it that way: with patience and experiment, various possibilities were considered and eliminated, and a course of action for the sequence was gradually built up. (Down on the middle platform, Robbie was lying under a sunshade and singing to himself, 'It's a Long Way to Tipperary.')

The morning's work was protracted and demanding. Twice Fotis and I broke off to plunge our heads under the Hippocratic fountain, but when the taxi returned at one o'clock, bringing Maureen with two large baskets full of lunch, the essential shots had all been taken. Retiring under the shady trees at the foot of the triple terrace, we dropped thankfully on to our elbows, and settled down to Maureen's special *risotto* and glasses of the local red wine. The taxi returned yet again, unloading an old lady in black together with a group of young girls ('Hurrah!' exclaimed Robbie, 'Lolitas!'), who stood chatting, giggling and eyeing us inquisitively, before tramping off across the fields to a local shrine. Replete and restored, we packed Maureen and her baskets back into the car, thanked young Costas warmly for his help, and

140

returned for two hours' 'fill-in' shooting of stones, inscriptions and landscapes.

That evening was our last in Cos. All along the waterfront the cafés – more Italianate and Riviera-like than the general run of Greek bars – buzzed and chattered with life from breakfast-time until midnight; and several rival juke-boxes were giving tongue throughout normal waking hours. The complement of the *Jack London* filled three tables at three separate cafés. Outside the southernmost bar Fotis and Maureen were laughing together, and from time to time Fotis would slip inside with a coin in his hand. The rest of us sat and sipped our yoghourt (or beer, or liqueurs, or Turkish coffee), making such conversation as was possible against the raucous juke-box background. The obstinate rhythms of the song *Mustafa* broke repeatedly over our heads, interspersed with something about 'a one-way ticket to the moon'. We shouted, argued, waved to acquaintances, swapped jokes, but in the end the barrage of noise was too much for us. We gave up the effort of talking, and sat silent, gazing across the glinting harbour at the shadowy walls of the castle.

Finally, Tom Crichton could stand it no more. Down in the harbour, these two insistent tunes had been blaring at him a dozen times a day throughout the last three days. Chuntering and muttering about the 'bloody juke-boxes', he stumped off back towards the boat. 'If I knew who was playing those bloody tunes,' we heard him say as he went, 'I'd bloody well shoot him. . . .' I looked round to order another cup of coffee, and noticed Fotis striding out of the next-door café, whistling and waving his arms like a conductor. He caught my eye. Two seconds later, the loudspeakers began shuddering out yet again the bash-bash-bash of *Mustafa*. . . .

★　　★　　★

Next day we turned North, and began to work our way through the remaining Dodecanese Islands towards Samos. At once, the extreme contrasts between these islands were impressed on us. At lunch-time, we lay becalmed off Pserimos, barely five miles from the northern tip of Cos. The island was waterless and deserted. A thin, pallid grass covered its triangle of hills, nourishing itself on the sparse rainwater alone. There was no sign of life. After lunch a fresh breeze got up, and we reached briskly across to Calymnos, arriving at six in the afternoon. As on Pserimos, many of the hills here were barren and brown, but two narrow valleys running up between them captured water enough to supply the busy port. Stretching three-quarters of the way across one of the bays a heavy jetty enclosed a crowded harbour, and on both flanks the hillside terraces were covered with houses washed over in a vivid and distinctive shade of blue. We tied up and went ashore. Here, the relaxed amiability of Cos was completely absent: the whole town struck one as on edge. Where the jetty joined the main quay, a political argument was in progress. Along the main waterfront, beyond a row of shops hung with sponges for sale, young couples were leaning on café tables in earnest, passionate conversation. Here and there older men, many of them mutilated, sat back over their drinks, puffing at their pipes and nodding anxiously. The entire population seemed to be out on the quay, walking up and down in nervous groups, their eyes darting about abstractedly as they talked together in a worried and less-than-animated way. Quite evidently, this was a community with something collectively on its mind.

We soon found out what it was. For us, Calymnos was only one port of call among others, a place to spend the night *en route*. Laden with big straw shopping-baskets, Fotis and Maureen (or, as we were coming to think of them, 'Fotis-and-Maureen') disappeared into the town to re-stock the ship's galley. After a brief reconnaissance ashore, however, the rest of us converged back on the boat, June and I pausing only at one shop where some particularly fine sponges were hanging on a string by the door. We selected three of them and went inside to ask the price. Half-a-dozen islanders were sitting around at tables, drinking coffee and *ouzo*. The shopkeeper looked at us for a moment, then tentatively tried out a price of 60 drachmas; but he was so obviously asking to be bargained with that it seemed only sporting to beat him down, and he accepted half that amount without protest. Someone shouted at him, evidently pulling his leg, and there was a burst of laughter. He shrugged his shoulders, laughed on one side of his face, and said: '*C'est le commerce.*' Coming out of the shop door, we fell in with Robbie, and exchanged impressions of the town: what he had to tell us explained completely the strain hanging over the port.

The island of Calymnos lives by – and for – sponges. As a piece of 'real estate', the island is a very poor proposition. On its few fertile and watered acres, it could support only a fraction of its actual population; and, if one leaves aside the few farmers and fishermen, everyone else on the island is dependent, directly or indirectly, on sponge-diving. At first, the men of Calymnos could find their sponges near at hand. With the passage of time, however, the main harvest has had to be sought further and further afield; and, by now, the most profitable and fertile colonies are those along the shores of North Africa. Collecting them involves a long expedition. The orange-painted sponge-boats, each with its golden star or bright eye painted on either bow, set off each year in the spring and return only in September or October; and, all too often, they come back with some of their divers crippled by the bends, or injured in the other hazards of the trade. For, as the men of Calymnos practise it, sponge-diving is still a primitive and dangerous craft. It calls for great strength and daring, and involves severe risks, especially for the impetuous.

What Robbie had discovered was this: that the departure of the sponge-boats – which we had already seen gathered in the harbour, gay in their fresh paint and trim with new rigging – was now only three days hence. The islanders, he told us, were entering the last phase of their apprehensive festivities. Every young man now fit, strongly muscled and ready for action, knew very well that he might come back six months hence having lost the use of his legs. That one there, gazing deeply into the eyes of his young bride – and few Greeks are ever so demonstrative in public – was aware that he might, perhaps, not come back at all. Every one of the islanders had some good reason for anxiety, either on his own account, or on that of his near relatives and friends. The cloud hanging over Calymnos was very real: it

143

was the same that a century ago, in the era of *Moby Dick*, hung over New Gloucester, New Bedford and the other whaling ports along Cape Cod.

We cleared from Calymnos early next morning, and rounded the headland to the West of the port. Once out to sea, we made due North along the shore of the island, helped by a south-westerly wind, and though the wind fell light later we were, by evening, at anchor in the fjord which serves Patmos as a harbour. The kaleidoscope had been shaken: another island presented us with quite another appearance. Patmos is a starfish of an island, sprawling on the water with the centre of its body humped up to a point, and all its arms lying out at awkward angles.

On the summit of the island stands the battlemented monastery of St John the Divine, or *Ayios Ioannes Theologos*, and the part played by sponge-diving at Calymnos is played at Patmos by . . . theology. For this is the home of the *Book of Revelation*. Here is the Cave of the Apocalypse, where – according to St John – a Voice from Heaven dictated his account of the End of All Things and the Last Judgment. Delayed in harbour by a re-currence of the *meltem*, we climbed the track up to the monastery, and were shown round by a *mondain* and well-groomed monk. Outside on the battlements, the sunlight leapt back from the white roofs of the town with double violence, so that we blinked in the glare. Inside, three older brethren sat over illuminated manuscripts: not studying them, we remarked sadly to ourselves, but merely numbering their pages in pencil. We were shown wonderfully decorated vestments – but in glass cases; the precious *Codex Purpureus*, with its early Greek capital script dark against the blood-red paper – but locked out of the reader's reach; and a library whose chief public exhibits were charters granted by Renaissance Dukes, Doges and Kings (of Savoy, Vaud, Venice or Cyprus), together with a visitors' book in which, with practised thumb, our guide turned up that day in 1910 when Patmos was honoured by a visit from Winston Churchill, together with Clementine and young Randolph.

Back on the quayside, a cloth-capped fisherman sat on the ground, leisurely mending a net. His friends addressed him as 'Sam

(a) *above* Storage-jars at Knossos
(b) *below* Spearing an octopus (Sitia)

9. CRETE

(a) *above* The Harbour
(b) *below* Turkish cemetery

10. COS

II. PATMOS: FRESCOES IN THE MONASTERY OF ST JOHN THE DIVINE

(a) *above* Backgammon
(b) *below* Drying nets

12. TIGHANI (PYTHAGORION) SAMOS

13. SAMOS: JUNE IN THE TUNNEL OF EUPALINUS (530 BC)

(a) *left* The central meeting-point, from the Northern half. Here the workers from the North had to deflect their tunnel, breaking through at an angle into the Southern half. (b) *right* The water-conduit from the tunnel to Tighani.

14. TUNNEL OF EUPALINUS, SAMOS

(a) *above* The valley of the Meander, from the city
(b) *below* The ancient harbour, now miles inland

15. PRIENE

(a) *above* Farmer of Sardis
(b) *below* Going home

16. TURKEY

Houston', and he confirmed that, although he was a native of Patmos, he had spent forty-three years in Texas. During that time, he had returned to the island precisely three times, first to marry and then to beget his children. (The family had stayed on in Greece when he was away.) Now he was back home for good, living on his pension from Social Security, and fishing only enough to earn his tobacco-money. Why go anywhere else? This was where he belonged. All his relatives were around him, so why stay in the States? He jerked his head towards the lower town, with its shops and cafés clustered around the port. We followed his glance, and from there looked up across the fertile slope leading to the Monastery: we saw his point. A small boy was paddling a fishing boat across the harbour: on its stern was painted the name – *Theologia*. One could certainly do worse than settle on Patmos. If we could only have stayed there a few days longer, and sampled more of its *douceurs*, we might have been tempted ourselves.

But we had business on Samos. By next morning the *meltem* had blown itself out, and we got away at eight. As we turned East from the mouth of the harbour-fjord, a school of dolphins picked up the boat and guided us to the corner of the island. Swift and sleek, they thrust themselves along powerfully, forcing past our bows and sheering away from within two feet of the *Jack London*'s planking. Having piloted us to the edge of the land, they turned away to the South, and we for our part made North-eastwards towards Samos.

It was a typically grey 'low-pressure' day, with negligible wind, so we had to keep motoring along under the diesel. Half-way across, we paused for lunch, and swam twice round the drifting boat; and by 4 p.m. we were coming up to Tigani. On our right hand, the Turkish coastline drew itself up into a prominent headland, formed by the twin, 4,000-foot peaks of Mount Mycale (or Samsun Dag). On our left hand, the island of Samos sloped gradually down from its own 4,000-foot western summit to the gentler shoreline of its Eastern Cape. Here a narrow strait (a bare mile across at its narrowest) separates Europe from Asia and, dominating the approach to the straits from its site at the foot of a small hill, we could already make out the buildings of the port.

In ancient times, Tigani was the principal town of Samos, and a considerable political power in its own right. June had worked here once before, with Fotis as her cameraman, so for them this visit was something of a homecoming. From her account and her photographs, I already knew a good deal about the circular harbour, with its long protective mole built on foundations originally laid out before 500 B.C. Harbour and mole, I recalled, combined into the form of a frying-pan, and this gave the town its name of *tigani* (or 'frying-pan') which it lost only recently, when an official decree re-christened it 'Pythagórion', to commemorate the 2,500th anniversary of the mathematician Pythagoras. As we coasted along off the bay to the West of the town, June pointed out the site of the Temple of Hera three miles southwest of Tigani: through binoculars, we could just make out a single column standing in isolation among the tumbled ruins. Then a little further on, scrutinizing the hillside behind the port, 'Yes: there it is,' she said, and pointed to a white speck of a building standing by itself half-way up the slope. That, she told us, marked the southern entrance to the Tunnel of Eupalinus, which it was our business to explore and photograph, as thoroughly as we could, in the course of the next few days.

Up to now, our journey had been consecrated mainly to the origins of scientific theory, but here at last was a striking monument from the history of engineering practice. Yet its presence off the Ionian shore was itself something which raised some fascinating questions. Was it by a chance of history that the tunnel was built just here in the sixth century B.C., on an island which had so recently given birth to Pythagoras, and which was within signalling range of Miletus? (For Miletus lies only fifteen miles away to the South-east.) Were the engineers who designed and constructed the tunnel exploiting the scientific ideas of the Ionians and the mathematics of Pythagoras? Were they – that is to say – proceeding like modern technologists; finding, in the novel theories of Greek science and mathematics, intellectual tools of use for their own, more practical ends? Or was this early exercise in

146

sophisticated technology yet another, independent manifestation of that originality and versatility which the Greeks displayed during those centuries of glory? About these questions, the single reference in Herodotus which is our sole literary evidence gives one no indication at all, and there were only two other possible sources of information. We could turn to the survey of the tunnel carried out in 1883 by the German archaeologist, Ernst Fabricius; or we could inspect the relics of the tunnel on the spot for ourselves. As a result of her earlier visit, June already had some fairly definite hunches. Now was our chance to check them.

Her old acquaintances at Tigani were expecting us somewhere around April 20th to 25th. It was now the 23rd. We rounded the end of the mole. As we approached the harbour entrance, we could see a Committee of Welcome assembling on the quay. We had evidently been observed. We braced ourselves to face another Greek reunion.

9 · The Dictator and the Engineer

———◦❧ ❧◦❧❧◦❧ ◦❧◦—

The tyrant Polycrates was in a quandary. During the years after 550 B.C. he had established himself on Samos as the first of the new-style autocrats. By a mixture of dash, aggression and alliances, he had won control of the Eastern Aegean. Power had brought him wealth and magnificence, Anacreon was his court poet, and the riches of the Hellenic world gravitated towards him. Even learning had some share of honour; though Pythagoras – like Einstein in a similar situation – emigrated across the seas to the New World in the West, and spent the last years of his life in the Greek colonies of Southern Italy.

Polycrates' capital was happily placed, on the south-east shore of the island. A natural harbour, protected from most winds, gave him complete command of the narrow straits between the island and the Ionian shore. The steep ridge behind the port (known today as Mount Castro) provided the town with a ready-made site for an Acropolis. Temples, theatres, houses rose in terraces above the harbour, and the vineyards and pastures alongside the city were as productive as any in the Aegean.

Yet the higher Polycrates rose, the more he feared. His success had been won only at a price: he had made enemies, and opulence had bred jealousy. His fantastic humours roused mixed feelings, among his allies as much as his opponents: he used to say that he enjoyed seizing his friends' boats even more than his enemies', since they were so much more grateful when he released them. Before long, he was beginning to fear – with some reason – that every man's hand was against him. So he became obsessed by the dream of all autocrats: the dream of making his position impregnable.

He completed the vast Temple of Hera, three miles down the

coast, in the hope of winning Divine favour. To divert the punishment for *hubris*, he cast his most precious ring into the sea. (This did him little good: according to legend, the ring reappeared soon after from the stomach of a fish which had been served up to him at dinner.) Finally, with the instincts of a modern dictator, he embarked on an elaborate programme of public works. He threw a circle of rugged fortifications around the city on its landward side, and their remains still span the crest of Mount Castro today. He built a great breakwater, 300 yards long, which made good the last natural weakness of his harbour. Yet there still remained, hanging over his head, one further threat – namely, Drought. The city itself contained no spring giving water all the year round; and the larger Polycrates' capital grew the less it could hope to survive on roof-top cisterns of rainwater alone.

In the surrounding countryside, there was only one wholly reliable and regular source of water: a spring at the modern village of Ayiades, which flowed – and still flows – strongly at all seasons. Ayiades lay well inland, up a valley, and could easily be defended. But it was fully 2,000 crow's-yards away, and the whole bulk of Mount Castro stood between Ayiades and Tigani. Evidently he must exploit that source of water somehow, but how was he to get it to the city? The obvious answer was to build a surface conduit to carry the water from the spring to the city, but to this there was a military objection. The conduit must pass round the western end of the hill and enter the city from outside, and such a line would be extremely exposed. A besieging army could block it at will: a daring raid from the sea could cut it. So Polycrates had to find some other way of getting the water he needed from Ayiades into Tigani.

Necessity is the mother of technology. Who conceived the grandiose project by which Polycrates attempted to cover his Achilles' heel? We do not know. His engineer (Herodotus tells us) was called Eupalinus, and came from Megara, between Athens and Corinth. Whoever was responsible, the solution adopted was a daring one. As in so many of the best devices, the key lay in turning the very obstacle to advantage; and the water-supply was finally protected by nothing less than the solid mass of Mount Castro itself.

The plan adopted was to drive a straight tunnel, 1,000 yards long, through the solid rock from one side of the hill to the other, so converting the barrier into an impenetrable shield. From spring to city, the whole watercourse was to be hidden below ground. From the spring, a stone channel carried the water by a round-about route, along the contours and under two stream-beds, delivering it at a point inside the upper mouth of the tunnel. On the other, southern side of the mountain, the tunnel debouched within the city perimeter, and fed the water into a network of pipes. These pipes eventually ran right down to the market-place and harbour, where they operated two elaborate water-clocks, showing the time and the date. Two hundred years later, Aristotle was sarcastic about the 'Polycratic works', quoting them as illustrations of the methods tyrants employ to keep their sub-jects out of mischief, and so maintain themselves in power. Hero-dotus on the other hand called the Tunnel, the Mole and the Temple 'the three greatest works of all the Greeks'. (But then, Herodotus himself was an Asiatic Greek from Halicarnassus, and so perhaps was prejudiced in favour of the Samians. At any rate, he was full of praise for the revolt against the Persians by which they regained their independence at a turning-point in the Graeco-Persian wars.) Either way, the Tunnel of Eupalinus was unique at the time, and it still remains a remarkable piece of engineering design. We already had some idea just how remarkable it was, from Fabricius' survey; and this was soon to be confirmed. For, when inspected on the ground, the tunnel turns out to have been driven from the two ends independently – like its modern counterpart under Mont Blanc – and the two halves met in the middle of the hill, with an error of only a few feet in either direction.

In this surprising accuracy lay the heart of our historical riddle. For there was no outside evidence to show how it had been achieved. Building the tunnel in this way involved four separate technical problems, none of them entirely straightforward. One had first to locate the entry-points on the two hillsides from which tunnelling was to begin, and then to fix the directions in which the teams of tunnellers must work in order that their two tunnels should meet; and both starting-point and direction had to be chosen both in the vertical (with an eye to relative heights) and in the horizontal. It was not enough for the tunnel to run (so to speak) along a dead straight line on the map: only if the heights of the two entrances were suitably chosen would the tunnel slope downwards at the angle needed to keep the water flowing with a reasonable head.

How were these crucial choices made? To take the easier leg of the problem first: in theory at any rate, one might suppose, the horizontal direction of the tunnel could be settled easily by applying geometrical principles of a kind that Pythagoras and his brighter pupils would have regarded as elementary. And certainly the idea looked fine on paper: one takes a map of the area, super-imposes on it a diagram showing the intended line of the tunnel, and constructs a series of 'similar triangles', by which (it is sug-gested) the directions of work at each end of the tunnel are to be determined. Historians of science and technology who have not visited the tunnel in person tend, in fact, to assume that the choice *must* have been made in this way.

Yet what would this procedure involve *in practice*? The sug-gestion is that Eupalinus and his colleagues worked their way round the slopes of Mount Castro from one entrance to the other by 'triangulation', and so provided themselves with leading marks to fix the direction of tunnelling. As June had noticed on her previous visit, this was easier said than done; and, for men who possessed no accurate maps, it would be a very dubious project indeed. The slopes of Mount Castro are rugged and so intersected by ravines that, even with modern instruments, surveying is a delicate task. To achieve any accuracy in this way at all, one would require a sighting-tube such as the *dioptra*, and this is believed to have come into general use a century or more after Polycrates' time. So might not Eupalinus and his colleagues have used some much simpler method to fix the relative hori-zontal positions of his two entrances – some purely practical method, independent of both high-grade cartography and

Pythagorean geometry? That was one thing we had to check; and beyond that there was a further and harder question – how they knew the difference in height between the two ends of their tunnel. The northern entrance is out of sight both of the sea (that natural horizon) and of the southern exit. Yet the results speak for themselves. As Fabricius's survey showed, the two halves of the tunnel reached the point of junction some fifteen feet apart in the horizontal but, in point of height, the floor of the northern half was only just above the ceiling of the southern half. How (we asked ourselves) could such precision have been achieved?

*   *   *

It was as well that we had plenty to do at Tigani: otherwise, we should have been marooned there for a week, kicking our heels. The morning after our arrival, it started blowing half-a-gale from the South-east, and for the next six days the wind swung to and fro across the southern half of the compass, with three days of intermittent heavy rain and thunderstorms on two of the nights. Things got so bad, in fact, that we retired inside the tunnel thankfully, reflecting that there (at any rate) we could get on with the job, rain or shine.

As soon as we could disentang'e ourselves from the Committee of Welcome, June and I set off for a quick reconnaissance. We walked out of town along the main street, past Pedro's new shop, and dropped Michel the telegraph clerk off at his office. Half-a-mile out of town, the foot of the ancient fortifications came down to the road. We clambered uphill beside them, until we were on a level with the southern exit of the tunnel. There was time only to glance inside the square marble building marking the spot. This looked more like a glorified potting-shed than anything else, and was erected in the 1880s, when Samos had succeeded in half-freeing itself from the Turks, and the autonomous province was considering a project to re-instate Eupalinus' water supply. Yes: there, just within the building, was the narrow slit of a stairway leading down underground into the southern half of the tunnel; fifty yards further east, and much overgrown, was the

152

outlet from which the water-conduit curved round to join the town water supply; and, from that point on, we could follow the track of the original stone conduit for several hundred yards.

As the conduit drops slowly down the contours towards the ancient city, the line of man-holes is still largely intact, and we followed them along, across fields and orchards, back towards the town. Just beyond the point at which we lost track of it, a small farmhouse stood under the almond-trees. As we passed the farmhouse, two women came out: we smiled, saluted them and exchanged monosyllabic conversation. They gestured to us to enter the house and we obeyed, expecting the customary gifts of water and jam. But no: what they had in store for us was something more striking and unusual. Pulling back the table and chairs into the corner of the room, the lady of the house uncovered a fine mosaic: a stag pursued by two dogs. It was Roman work to all appearances, and a very attractive example at that. On a pleasant wooded slope, facing south over the sea, and with an assured water-supply: this was just the kind of place a sensible colonial official from the Province of Asia might have chosen for his summer villa. As I now recalled, Eupalinus' water-course remained in use for many centuries, and survived the Roman period. Indeed the Romans supplemented it by building a further conduit above ground, from a more distant source: this crossed the Ayiades valley by an aqueduct and continued round the hillside, to join Eupalinus' conduit just outside the southern mouth of the tunnel. But the women were trying to explain something. What was that? '*Loutra*,' they were saying, '*loutra Pythagorou*'. Yes, I might have guessed – the local name for the mosaic was 'the Baths of Pythagoras'!

Until we had some effective means of lighting it, there was no hope of filming inside the tunnel, and we had arranged for a portable generator to be sent direct from Athens. This, however, was not due for thirty-six hours, so we spent the next morning reconnoitring around the harbour. It was not until the afternoon that June and I returned to the tunnel, together with Fotis. Torches in hand, we squeezed our way down the narrow staircase and entered the passage leading into the hill: this was less than two feet wide, and only some five feet high.

On either side, the passage was shored up with archaic stone-work reminiscent of Mycenae: pairs of simple rough-cut slabs, propped against one another to form a gable overhead. Twelve yards along, a square ventilation-shaft opened overhead, casting a patch of light on to the walls and floor, and immediately beyond this we left the layer of topsoil, passing through an ancient door-way into the main tunnel. We emerged into a large chamber chiselled out of solid rock. Straight in front of us, a precipitous trench some twenty-five feet deep ran diagonally across the chamber and out of sight to the right – where, no doubt, it originally joined up with the external conduit to the town. Across this ditch a small concrete slab had been laid, and in an alcove to the left there was a rough semi-circular seat, together with small ledges on which small pottery oil-lamps could have been propped. Immediately beyond the little bridge, the trench straightened out and got down to business. From this point on, the tunnel was very nearly square in cross-section, varying between five and seven feet in height and breadth. A little way ahead we could see another alcove, cut into the rock on the left – the sort of place where workmen might have stored their tools; otherwise, the tunnel stretched away and away, shrinking in the distance for as far as the beams of our torches would reach. For as far as we could see, equally, the ditch carrying the water-conduit could be made out, reappearing every few yards along the right-hand side of the tunnel.

We began to work our way slowly up the tunnel. The water-channel had originally been carried in rectangular clay pipes, and in places the trench was covered over, but in other places it was still left gaping, leaving exposed to view a vertical rock wall as high as a house. We picked our way cautiously: the tunnel would present no real difficulties to an experienced potholer, but the path along the left-hand side seemed very narrow to beginners like us, and besides, as we got further into the mountain, it became very muddy and slippery.

Fabricius, writing in 1883, gave a very good account of the

construction of Eupalinus' tunnel. From this, we knew that the trench was only four feet deep at the northern entrance to the tunnel, and increased steadily in depth towards the southern end. Probably it did not form part of the original plan: the labour involved in cutting out a twenty-five foot ditch could well have been spared. Maybe Eupalinus underestimated the gradient needed to keep the water flowing copiously, and failed to drive the southern half of the tunnel low enough down; so that, after having finished the main tunnel, the workers were compelled to go back and excavate an additional steeper ditch to carry the waterpipes.

Whatever the reason, there the trench was, gaping ominously to our right, and asking to be fallen into. (There have in fact been some serious accidents recently, as a result of visitors missing their footing.) Between the sections of trench, there lay piles of old potsherds – fragments of the ancient piping hauled up out of the ditch in the 1880s. After 150 yards or so, we struck a particularly slippery patch: here, water was continually seeping in from the surrounding hill, and making the path dangerous. Further on (according to Fabricius) there should be a great deal to see – notably, the remains of a Byzantine shrine, and the actual point of junction between the two halves of the tunnel. Still, better safe than sorry: we decided to retreat for the moment, and come back another day better shoed and prepared.

In memory the next six days remain as a mosaic of images – café, hotel, harbour, tunnel, hillside and café again, jostling together in a random pattern. Here, for instance, we are sitting round a square wooden table at the quayside bar, and arguing about the construction of the tunnel. Michel from the Telegraph office is slender and still in his twenties, but already beginning to go bald; his friend Dhaskalis, the schoolmaster, is slightly sceptical (like the schoolmaster in a French film), but has also the twinkling eye and the neat moustache of a would-be man-about-town; Costas, the young taxi-driver, has a jolly, dimpled face and fair wavy hair; the Harbour Master, in white cap and navy uniform, is inclined to pontificate, with a consciousness of his own official status; Manoli, the local odd-job man, with his sharp-cut features and dark, crinkly hair, has attached himself to our party after the manner of Comna at Chrysso. On the outskirts, there sit other figures: Manoli's attractive wife, Poppy, and their small daughter, Ticky – Calliope and Grammatike to you; Plato, the hotel-keeper, who is planning to sell up his interests in Samos and move permanently to his other home in Brooklyn; and finally, in the background, the khaki-uniformed figure of the Customs Officer. (He is ill at ease, not being a native of Tigani: his job alone has brought him here, and he does not really belong.) Can we get some record of local café-life on film? Why, surely: the café owner knows a team of *bouzouki* players, and will arrange for them to be at the café tomorrow evening, so that we can all have a party. (Tomorrow comes, but – alas – no *bouzouki* players: the proprietor explains sadly that they have been playing at a wedding in the next village of Choria, and are out of action for the day....)

The picture changes. We have set up a base of operations in Plato's hotel – single room 20 drachmas a night, double room 30 drachmas: i.e. one dollar. Each evening at six o'clock, the electric generator starts up and the lights of the town go on until half-past-eleven or midnight: we plug the trickle-charger in and start the camera-motor batteries recharging. The hotel is at the western end of the quay. The balcony bears the grand inscription 'Hotel Pythagorian': when we step out onto it, we have a fine view right along the curve of the harbour, past where the *Jack London* is moored stern to quay, and the café where Tom Crichton sits over a drink and taps at his typewriter. (Since reaching Samos he has experienced a change of life: his beard has come off, and he has begun to write a novel based on his gruelling experiences as the Majorca representative of a holiday-tour agency.) To the right, several fishing-boats are hauled up on land beside a capstan, and beyond them Polycrates' mole is aimed like an arrow across the water at the heart of Mount Mycale. The weather having turned foul, I put on my windjammer and go out along the mole, where the roaring sou'wester is throwing up great breakers. All I get for my pains is a drenching for myself and my camera.

The picture switches again. We are back in the tunnel, with the generator and lights that two of Alec's technicians have brought from Athens. The ghost of Eupalinus is unco-operative. After the violent thunderstorm overnight, there is rain in the air, and we have to rig a waterproof covering over the generator. It takes quite a time to get all the lights fixed up, but finally Fotis is satisfied. By one o'clock, everything is in position and we are ready to go. The plugs are switched on and the scene is transformed. No one can ever have seen the tunnel looking like this before – not even its makers. During its 2,500 years of existence the walls of the tunnel have become coated with a fine layer of mineral deposit: in places this growth branches like trees, at others it gleams in sheets of hard, smooth skin, or drips from the roof in miniature stalactites. (These growths become larger the further one goes into the hill, and eventually they help to block the way entirely.) Now, in the dazzling light, the square passage runs away and away before us, opalescent walls glinting where the light picks up the newly-forming crystals. Apart from some large pink spiders there is no sign of life. The spiders stir uneasily in the novel brilliance, and the water-trench – for once well lit – yawns beside us, with its full depth clearly visible.

We run off a test-roll of film, but decide to break for lunch before shooting the main bulk of our material. Maureen has brought up another of her excellent picnics, so we return above ground and sit around beside the generator. Eupalinus, however, has not finished with us. We pack away lunch, start up the generator motor and return underground. We go to switch on the lights, but there is not a volt to be had. The dynamo is quite dead and resists all attempts to resuscitate it. We do some desultory shooting around the entrance to the tunnel, while the technicians strip down the generator hoping to diagnose the fault and repair it. Then, out of nowhere, three incongruous figures stumble on the scene – it is the local Marx Brothers, the café-owner's team of *bouzouki* players, who are shaking off their hangovers by walking the five miles across country from Choria to Tigani. They gambol zanily about, do cartwheels and handsprings, chase each other crazily around the tunnel entrance, and finally disappear off towards the village.

Emerging grimily from under the generator, Alec's assistants bring us bad news: there is a short-circuit in the dynamo which will have to go back to Athens for repair. Eupalinus has certainly got his own back. We look around us – what are we to do now? One thing catches our eye. On the plain below us, the Greek Army is at work, constructing a new airfield. There lies our last hope, for perhaps they have a suitable generator, and can be induced to lend it to us. All those days in Athens spent in courtesy-calls, all that labour collecting authorizations and letters of recommendation, at last justify themselves. We dig out as many imposing documents as we can, and send Robbie off to see what can be managed.

Next day: June and I have persuaded a photographer from Vathy, which is the chief town of modern Samos and lies over the hills from Tigani, to lend us his flashlight equipment: we want to take still photographs right in the heart of the mountain. The photographer is anxious to supervise our use of his equipment, and has insisted on coming with us. Never having entered the tunnel before, he arrives for the occasion rather overdressed. June and I put on an air of absolute confidence and plunge boldly ahead into the hill, barely stopping until we are some 400 yards inside. With *philotimia* to consider, our friend from Vathy turns a blind eye to the unforeseen fears and discomforts of the expedition, and follows bravely behind. At last we reach the point where Fabricius found evidence of a Byzantine shrine, or chapel; but here the floor is covered with water a foot deep, and our friend has had enough. Entrusting the precious flashlight to us, he squats in the tunnel and tells us to go ahead. Two square slabs lie against the wall of the tunnel, one of them decorated with a geometrical border and a deeply-incised cross, while several small marble columns have collapsed on to the tunnel floor. The mineral deposits of 1,000 years have already gone a long way towards reclaiming these stones: by now, stalactites envelope them, and they are once again solidly united with the rocky earth. We press on another fifty yards and arrive at the point of junction. The water ditch turns to the left through a right-angle, and for some way the tunnel runs uphill in a wavering curve, before getting back on line again. Evidently the workmen coming from the North heard their collaborators cutting away at the rock from the South, and effected the actual meeting only after several changes of direction. We continue some way past the junction but, while we are draped in flash-lamps and the rest, the debris and stalactites make it impossible to go very far. We pick our way back to the chapel, to find our photographer sitting in the dark and muttering to himself, 'Never again!'

It is an evening later in the week. We are back at the café, and are subsidizing a party for our friends and colleagues at the port. Alec's assistants have dumped the ailing generator, and tethered two floodlights to the town mains. Fotis has arranged the camera and lights, so that he can photograph the goings-on in the café. The Marx Brothers are finally disintoxicated and playing vigorously. Manoli, the odd-job man, is dressed as a fisherman. He starts on a solo dance which – *ouzo* by *ouzo* – becomes progressively more animated and violent. Inside the café, I have linked up the portable tape-recorder to a microphone, and this is propped insecurely on a chair beside the *bouzouki* players. (I hope they keep reasonably sober.) The music increases in pace, and a communal frenzy begins to take hold. June is sitting at a table with Michel, Dhaskalis and Costas: they are all laughing and clapping in time to the music. Now Manoli sweeps one of the young fishermen into his dance and they embark on a duet. There is a burst of laughter from the tables as their motions become, first suggestive, then recognizable, and finally downright obscene. After a time, even Fotis cannot stand it any longer. He snaps off the camera-motor, wrinkles his face and turns away, with his hands over his eyes, torn between disgust and laughter: 'I couldn't photograph *that*!'

After the homosexual Turkish duet, the dancing becomes general. Ouzo, dried octopus, ouzo, coffee, ouzo: the party food continues to circulate. By eleven-thirty things are beginning to get . . . well, undignified: glasses are being thrown to the ground and scrunched underfoot. Still, no need to worry: the generator will soon be closing down for the night. We wind the party up, and settle the café-owner's bill. (Five pounds covers the lot.) Soon the cameras and lights are packed away, and the revellers are spiralling up the main street arm-in-arm, still singing to the last of the *bouzouki* music. June and I wander out onto the mole, under the stars. It has been quite a day: starting with a yet more violent thunderstorm at five in the morning, and involving several hours filming both around and positively *in* the harbour – with us in our bathing-costumes, and the camera-tripod liberally covered with grease. We sit down on a bollard – that is to say, on the broken drum of an antique column, looking across the harbour and town towards the shadowy slope of Mount Castro. The generator is switched off, and the last street-lamps along the quay flicker and go out. We are left in the moonlight, gazing over the trees and houses to the rocky hill whose puzzles we have still not entirely unravelled. A last snatch of song and guitar reaches us on the night breeze.

★   ★   ★

There were some questions about the Tunnel of Eupalinus which we could answer only by going round to the far end, to see how the water was brought from the Ayiades spring to the North entrance, and so into the mountain. Two years before, June had made the trip round Mount Castro with the help of an old refugee farmer from Asia Minor, known to everyone at Tigani as Baba Giorgios or Uncle George. We asked after him but were told that he was away at Choria, tending his tobacco-patch, so we arranged to set off the next morning under other, less picturesque auspices. We assembled on the quayside at about half-past-eight and were loading up one of the mules when our newly-appointed guide arrived. At once he leapt on a second mule, and galloped it up and down the main street, spurring it on so that it bucked and reared like an unbroken colt. Fotis groaned and clasped his brow, fearing for his beloved cameras – 'No good, Tom Mix!' he cried out, and chased the young man away indignantly. So there we were, with two mules but no guide.

At this moment, June gave a shout, 'Look! There's Uncle George,' and ran across the road to intercept him as he disappeared into the nearest bar for his breakfast *ouzo*. Ten minutes later the mules were loaded and we were off, making our way up the first slopes of the hillside, under the almond-trees and past the Baths of Pythagoras. We climbed to the tunnel-exit, then scrambled over Polycrates' fortifications and so on, traversing the rocky hillside and turning inland up the Ayiades ravine. The further we went, the more sceptical I became of the theory that Eupalinus triangulated his way round the hillside, establishing his directions of tunnelling at the two ends by applying the geometry of similar triangles. The terrain was rough and irregular; he would have been obliged to repeat the operation a dozen times or more; and, on this rugged hillside, it would have been near-impossible to mark out horizontal distances accurately.

Half-way up the ravine, beyond the tumbledown arches of the Roman aqueduct, the valley took a sharp turn to the right before zig-zagging inland again. We stopped beside the track for a rest and a bite of lunch, looking down across the scrub of oleanders growing in the base of the valley. By now I was thoroughly convinced: however else Eupalinus did the job, it was inconceivable that he should have worked his way, triangle by triangle, right round the hill and up this winding ravine. We continued up the valley another quarter of a mile, to where it widened out below the village of Ayiades. Somewhere on the hillside to the right, June remembered discovering the tunnel entrance two years ago. It was tucked well away and we took some time to locate it again. The first indication that we were on the right track came when we discovered the hole by which the waterpipe itself had entered the hillside; and a little later we all but fell into the tunnel entrance proper.

This time there was no marble potting-shed, no carefully-built flight of steps, no well-constructed entrance passage. We simply slid in, through the brambles and down a stone-filled chute, and plopped out into the tunnel on our feet, at the point where the water-conduit entered it from the left. Here the ditch (as Fabricius had reported) was barely four feet deep. Ahead, the tunnel had to be built through a much thicker layer of topsoil, and its walls were bricked up on either side, to give it extra strength – the brickwork apparently dated from Roman times. Clambering ahead, we reached the solid rock only after some eighty or a hundred yards, beyond a large pile of obstructing debris. A little way further on the stalactites began to fill the tunnel again, and we retreated. From this point on, the construction was clearly similar to what we had seen earlier, when coming from the south.

We had still to visit Ayiades village, whose unfailing spring had been the excuse for all this thought and labour. By the time the mules were reloaded, the day was far gone, and we made our way for the last half-mile in the late afternoon sun. The ancient reservoir now lies in the foundations of the local chapel, but the spring water still gushes out of a pipe into a pool, and so down the valley of oleanders. Another half-hour, and our work was finished. Fotis and Uncle George set off back to Tigani down the valley by which we had come, but June and I were still curious about Eupalinus' scheme, and decided to return by a different route.

To begin with, we followed the line of the ancient watercourse from the spring towards the North side of Mount Castro. For a couple of hundred yards it was almost lost in the fields and orchards of Ayiades. We could locate it unmistakeably only by looking for its intersection with the narrow tributary stream which runs westwards around the back of the hill and joins the main valley below Ayiades. At the point where he reached this stream, Eupalinus actually led his water-conduit *under* the stream-bed, and the square stone construction of the aqueduct is still clearly apparent, dipping below the brook. Twenty yards further South, we picked up another inspection-hole, of the sort familiar to us from the stretch of conduit at the town end of the conduit, and from there on we could follow the line of the watercourse with ease. By this time, however, the day was nearly over and we had to break off. If we were to get back across Mount Castro before dark, we must start now, so we began scrambling up the hill through a belt of trees, and on across open heathland towards the fortifications on the crest.

The northern end of the watercourse had been pretty well hidden, and the security of the whole arrangement depended on

162

its remaining so. The secret was well kept during Polycrates' own lifetime. (Despite all his efforts, he came to a violent end, being captured in battle in 522 B.C., and crucified by his enemies.) For a century, indeed, the fortress remained apparently invulnerable. But such a secret cannot be kept for ever. Having won their freedom from the Persians, the men of Samos allied themselves with the Athenians, only to end by antagonizing their fellow-Greeks. For, after a time, they sensed the attractions of neutralism, and tried to renounce the Athenian alliance; but – then as now – a small power, caught between two greater powers, declares itself neutral only at its own risk. Pericles of Athens was not prepared to allow the Samians the luxury of neutrality and laid Tigani under siege. Confident about their supplies of food and water, the inhabitants held out against him for several months. But the conduit was not, after all, one-hundred-per-cent secure. Pericles – the story goes – offered to call off his campaign, on condition that the Samians would give him a hostage for their future good behaviour. In return (it was Dhaskalis who told us the story, seated at his usual table outside the harbour café) the inhabitants of Tigani voted to send him their most crotchety alderman – a man of whom they were heartily glad to be rid. But the victim of this decision soon got his own back, by betraying them. Having no taste for exile, he revealed to Pericles the location of the underground channel linking the Ayiades spring to the tunnel. This pipe was quickly interrupted, and the fortress was obliged to surrender.

After the storms earlier in the week, the day had for once been fine and warm. We climbed slowly, for we were hot and tired. Coming out above the tree-line, we saw the sheer walls of Polycrates' outlying forts strung out along the crest of the slope above us. Another twenty minutes, and we were scrambling through a gap in the ancient fortifications. For a short way we kept along the line of the wall, then made diagonally across the hilltop to come out above the town. The orange globe of the sun had just dipped below the western hill-line, but out to sea the sky was still bright and clear. All along the horizon the nearer Dodecanese were pencilled in dark against the edge of the sea. If anything, I thought, it was far *too* clear: more bad weather tomorrow. The dusk soon began. We started to drop down the hillside, but found before long that we were too far to the east: our way was blocked by a series of steep screes and rocky cliffs, overgrown with rough thorny scrub. Yet there was no time to go back, and start the descent again further West: we had to clamber down where we were, as best we could, picking our way carefully from rock to rock, from tree to tree, and making use of whatever footholds and handholds presented themselves. Sliding, slipping, scrambling, we at last came – to our relief – onto the track leading from the South exit down to the harbour.

As we looked back through the gathering dark at the rugged stretch of hillside we had just negotiated, the solution of our chief problem flashed into my mind. For, as I now saw, we had failed hitherto to ask one crucial question: namely, Why did Eupalinus build the tunnel so far West? Why should he have gone to the trouble of leading his conduit back in a hairpin from the tributary brook to the Northern mouth, only to bring the tunnel out on the South side a full half-mile from the town? Strategically speaking, the whole construction could with advantage have been built considerably further East: indeed, if the Southern exit had been brought out nearer the centre of the town, Polycrates could then have shortened the perimeter wall around his city.

Once one saw the answer to this new question, a great light was thrown on our whole problem. For Eupalinus had, in fact, located the tunnel exit as near to the city as he could, without getting involved in the cliffs and screes by which we had ourselves so nearly been trapped. From his own chosen exit, one could climb without difficulty, straight up over the hill and down the other side to Ayiades. One could, in fact, set up a line of poles all the way across the hilltop from one mouth to the other. And this – I now saw – is what Eupalinus almost certainly did. In that way he needed no complicated survey whatever: all he required was a gross or so of wooden posts (say) ten feet high, which could be driven into the ground every fifteen or twenty yards, up, across and down the hill. It was impossible, of course, to see the one entrance from the other, but nowhere on the hill could one see less than six or eight of these posts, and for much of the way one could see many more.

After that, it was simply a question of getting the posts aligned. The direction of a line marked out in this way could be established by eye, to within perhaps $\frac{1}{2}°$ or $1°$ either way; and this was all the accuracy actually achieved in the finished tunnel. (The point of junction was some five yards out horizontally, at a point 500 yards into the hill.) Operating further East, on the other hand, Eupalinus would have found the cliffs and screes a serious obstacle, preventing one from establishing a continuous line over the brow of the hill. For, without seeing at least three posts at any one time, one cannot hope to maintain even a roughly constant direction, and in places the line of cliffs above the town would have made even this impossible.

The more I thought about it, the more likely it seemed that Eupalinus used some such straightforward procedure. Though the problem facing him was in some ways a novel one, it was, after all, a typical engineering problem, and did not obviously cry out for sophisticated theoretical analysis. In any case, Eupalinus was clearly a man with a genius for those simple devices which make engineering something of a fine art. How, for instance, did he make sure that the workers inside the tunnel kept digging in a constant direction? We had already answered this question for ourselves. It is one thing, of course, to establish the line you want to follow along the surface; but it is a very different matter to keep to this line below ground, working in near darkness with only oil lamps to light your way. The answer showed us something of Eupalinus' ingenuity. For, as we soon noticed, the square shaft in the entrance-passage at the South end was not there for ventilation alone: the pool of light below it was visible all the way along the southern half of the tunnel. From time to time, the line of the wall began to curve away slightly from the straight, but it always led back again; and however far in we went, we need only look over our shoulder to see far behind us – remote but reassuring – the spot of light at the foot of the shaft.

All that Eupalinus had to do, then, was to line his poles up over the ventilation-shaft and establish within the entrance-hall of the southern half a guiding-line matching in direction the line of the overland poles. Once that was done, it was necessary only to control the direction of work carefully for the first fifty yards or so: after that, the workmen would simply continue along the same line by keeping the light from the ventilation-shaft always in sight. This technique represented a great improvement over that employed in the only comparable tunnel we know older than the Tunnel of Eupalinus. The Tunnel of Hezekiah, outside Jerusalem, was kept in line only by probing upwards at intervals through the overburden of soil: as a result, it zig-zags several times, and reaches its destination only by trial and error.

One question remained: how the relative heights of the two entrances were fixed. Looking back later, I saw that this was not, perhaps, as hard a task as I had at first supposed. As my colleague Derek Price pointed out, the Greeks of the sixth century B.C. had no difficulty in constructing water-levels anything up to fifty feet long, with which Eupalinus could have marked out around the sides of Mount Castro a series of points at any chosen height: this procedure would introduce errors of less than $1°$ on each leg of the survey. Yet, once again, Eupalinus probably did the job even more simply. As we knew, there was some evidence of miscalculation in the vertical – *viz*. the depth of the trench added to the tunnel in order to carry the water-pipes. So, very possibly, he relied for his height-estimates also on the line of posts over the hill, keeping a rough running check on the heights gained and lost in going from one side to the other by measuring off the base of each pole against the next one below. On the seaward side, one could do this with a fair accuracy, by using the horizon out to sea to provide one with a level. Yet, even on the inland slope of the hill, the same operation could be carried out with errors of no more than a few inches for each step, so establishing the relative heights of the North and South entrances to within, at most, ten feet. The really tricky problem was one, not of surveying, but of engineering: to ensure that the tunnel floor sloped downwards from North to South at a suitable angle. It now looked as though Eupalinus did not face that particular problem directly, but constructed the main tunnel first – driving

166

it in two halves from each end, at a roughly-estimated slope – and adjusted the angle of fall only later, when the time came to lay the pipes, by digging out the trench until the water flowed fast enough.

In any event, there was no place in the story for Pythagoras. Local folk-heroes, of course, tend to get the credit for all the marvels in and about their native land. If the peasants of Tigani could unquestioningly credit Pythagoras with the authorship of a Roman mosaic, it was perhaps understandable that scholars should try to associate his ideas with the Tunnel of Eupalinus – this, after all, was built during his lifetime, dating from around 530 B.C. Yet there has never been any positive evidence to connect Eupalinus and Pythagoras; and now, after scrutinizing the tunnel on the ground, I doubted whether there ever would be. The tunnel is a great feat of engineering technique, but it need have involved no *theoretical* problems at all.

Polycrates – pirate, autocrat, dictator, tyrant, call him what you will – was the man who commissioned the tunnel. Eupalinus of Megara was the man who designed it. But who performed the actual hard labour of building it? About this, history tells us nothing, and we can only guess. Did Polycrates succeed in whipping his own reluctant citizens into doing the work for him? Certainly he was not universally popular among his own subjects: his autocratic attitudes gave offence, and Pythagoras reputedly left for Italy protesting that it was outrageous for Polycrates to set himself up as 'a man above other men'. Was the tunnel, in effect, one more product of Polycrates' piratical exploits? Did he treat the ships' crews that he captured as prisoners-of-war, and was it they who hacked out underground those hundred thousand cubic feet and more of solid rock? Remembering how, even in nineteenth-century Britain, the Napoleonic prisoners-of-war were exploited as cheap labour for public works, this seemed to me more than likely. But, whoever the labourers were, they left no signs of their identity, no *graffiti*, no autographs, no incised cries of protest . . . so that was one question which might very well *never* be answered.

★   ★   ★

We got back to the *Jack London* in time for a late supper. The Army had finally agreed to oblige. After engaging in protracted negotiations and making several telephone calls to Athens, Robbie had persuaded them to lend us a generator, so that we could finish our filming inside the tunnel next day. Eupalinus, it is true, had one more blow in store for us: the processing-laboratory in England failed to handle the film according to our instructions, so that much of our material ended up with a heavy 'grain'. But the worst was over: after six days, the bulk of our work on Samos was completed, and we could prepare for the next stage – and the climax – of our journey.

There were still minor mishaps ahead. Next morning, for instance, we returned to the *J.L.* hot and thirsty, after filming along the quay. Impulsively, I grabbed a lemonade-bottle from the deck, unstoppered it and drank deeply. Greedily gulping down the first mouthful, I discovered – too late – that the bottle contained, not lemonade, but some petrol or gasoline mixture used for odd jobs around the boat. I could have been much worse off: as things were, I was merely uncomfortable. Strong saline solution, mustard, olive oil – nothing would coax the fluid up again. I spent the rest of the day belching and reeking of gasoline vapour, while the rest of the crew took good care not to strike matches too close to my mouth.

The next stop would be Kushadasi, in Turkey; though why in Heaven's name anyone should *want* to go to Turkey, none of our friends at Tigani professed to understand. They themselves would never *dream* of going – openly, at any rate. Smuggling was a different matter, of course, since there were wild pig in the woods of Mount Mycale, and the wretched Turks (being Muslims) had silly prejudices about eating them. Pig-smuggling apart, they asked, what could possess anyone to visit that Godforsaken place? In all these protestations, there was no doubt an element of exaggeration, and of sour grapes. Rather late in the day, we discovered that we had no courtesy-flag to fly on arrival in Turkish waters. Dhaskalis tossed his head back knowingly, and told us not to worry: he would get us the loan of one if we would promise to bring it back without fail. He also moderated his theoretical Turkophobia to the extent of passing on the name and address of a pen-friend at Kushadasi – a young Turkish stamp-collector with whom he exchanged duplicates.

The element of sour grapes was pardonable. On the outskirts of Tigani was a cluster of houses in which, nearly forty years later, refugees like Uncle George still lived. This was a perpetual re-minder of that tremendous upheaval, in 1922–3, when the Greeks of Asia Minor fled before the troops of Ataturk and, after an era of 3,000 years, Anatolia finally lost its Hellenic character. It was not easy to sit there, a mere mile off shore, to see every day across the forbidden waters mountains, capes, rivers and villages whose Greek names were still well-remembered, and to know that they were lost to one's country and one's people – probably for ever.

These straits, over which Polycrates exercised his piratical control, have always been a strategic point on the map. In the classical period, when navigation meant primarily coast-hopping, they were a bottle-neck through which all the Asia Minor trade had to pass: no wonder Polycrates found Tigani a highly profitable base of operations. As late as the 1880s, Fabricius was encouraging the authorities on Samos to reinstate Eupalinus' watercourse, on the grounds that it would 'ensure a rich supply of healthy drinking water for the port of Tigani, a port becoming more and more im-portant every year'. Tigani has disappointed Fabricius' expecta-tions, for the regular port of Samos is now the deepwater anchor-age of Vathy on the North coast, and the Straits of Samos have become the boundary between two continents, not only in law and geography, but in national sentiment also. Tigani is now the last island outpost of Europe. Across the narrow straits, the Dip Burnu, formed by the foothills of the Samsun Dag – the Trogili-um Promontory, that is to say, formed by the western spur of Mount Mycale – is a western extremity of the Asiatic land-mass. Ionia is no longer, in any sense, a part of Hellas, and the Greeks just over the water – not surprisingly – find this fact hard to admit.

Still, their griefs were not our direct concern. Our only problem was how to get ourselves across to Kushadasi. The matter was not entirely simple. We had already placed our car in bond at the

Piraeus, as a condition of getting an exit permit, and now we were anxious not to take absolutely all our film equipment into Turkey. This meant depositing the balance in the care of the Customs Officer at Tigani. Then there were police to be visited at Vathy, reams of paper-work with the immigration authorities, last negotiations with the Harbour Master, and so on, and so on. Driving to and fro the five miles between Tigani and Vathy, we became freshly aware how much of a mark the Turkish occupation had left here – the old cemetery up the hill from Vathy, with its square enclosing-wall and pencil-sharp cypresses at each corner; the aspect of the houses above Vathy, with their characteristic Turkish balconies shaded under the eaves; even the Turkish-trousered country folk, going about their work in the fields.

Eventually the formalities were complete: we had been legally processed and packaged, and were ready for the inter-continental transit. But what sort of reception should we get the other side? We were seized with the impulse to telephone the Consul-General at Izmir, who had been interceding with the Turkish authorities on our behalf. This was easier said than done. Michel put on his most professional look, applying himself with enthusiasm to the mysteries of the Greek telephone system. It might seem a small matter to us to communicate with a country which we could almost touch. But if we supposed that Samos now had any material links with the mainland, less than a mile away, that was our mistake. No: Tigani had to be linked with Vathy, Vathy with Athens, Athens with Istanbul, and Istanbul with Izmir. Only when this Chestertonian network had at long last been completed, should we be in a position to talk to the Consul-General. Talk to him? . . . For that, it was necessary that he should *hear* us. Faint and crackling, his voice came back across the wire: his voice had shrunk to a distorted whisper, he was shouting that he could not hear who we were or what we were saying. Third time round Helen made momentary contact, and he gathered – or guessed – who we were. 'Yes,' replied a hoarse crackle, 'you are expected': but a crescendo of interference now drowned his voice irrevocably, and we hung up.

There was nothing else we could do . . . nothing, that is, except sit at the café with Michel and Dhaskalis and Costas and Plato and the Harbour Master and the Customs Officer, all of whom were ready to commiserate with us over our misfortune at leaving Greece for That Place. 'Never mind,' we replied: 'give us a week, and we'll be back.' They smiled, a little doubtfully – on one side of their faces only – 'If God wills', and signalled for another *ouzo*.

10 · The Deserted Birthplace

Deep-frozen over the peaks of the Balkans, the *meltem* aligns itself down the fingers of Chalcidice and launches out across the Aegean, with nothing to check it but the lonely Alcatraz of Ayios Evstratios. By-passing Lesbos, it accelerates across the empty sea, to meet the Asiatic mainland at the straits of Chios. Once through that bottleneck, it picks up speed again along the shore line past Kushadasi, where the *Jack London* pitches uneasily in the short sea, and collides head-on with the wooded slopes of the Samsun Dag above the site of Panionium. Crossing the mountain ridge at the 3,000-foot line, it gathers together its strength, and focuses itself with renewed force down the gulleys of the hillside on to the lonely ruins of Priene; then it gallops blusteringly away to the South-east, across the broad fenlands of the Meander delta. Shivering under the violence of the wind, the new year's grasses bow their heads, dipping to and fro across the unchanging stones. The founding fathers are dead, and their descendants have departed. Yet the ivy still clambers up and over the carved inscriptions, the heart-shaped incisions of its delicate leaves framing, in a land grown strange, the undying Greek message – *Evtycheite* – 'Be Happy, May You Prosper.'

Just beyond the village of Doganbey, we park, get out and leave our two young guides to doze in the little Renault microbus. Making our way along the grass track which leads up the hill-side towards Priene, we come out onto the first spur of the hill, and tussle with the cold wind. Some way ahead, a caterpillar of small black figures is just cresting the line of the main city wall. June and I, carrying some of the lighter equipment, get our breath back and plunge on again up the hill, followed in turn by Michael, our young English interpreter from Istanbul, and by

Fotis, who has insisted on carrying the heavy tripod and camera. To begin with there is not much to be seen. The walls and buildings of Priene, their outlines softened by the overgrowth of centuries, appear from below little more than natural outcrops on the mountainside. But, as we get nearer, the gates of the city open themselves before us, and we enter into the skeleton of a forgotten town.

Forgotten? Well not entirely . . . the crawling line of figures ahead of us resolves itself into a party of Turkish schoolchildren, who swarm over the city wall like ants on the frame of an abandoned honeycomb. Their black uniform cotton smocks, and their globular heads cropped close to the scalp, make them look as though they are on parole from some infant penitentiary. (There comes into my mind the memory of an autobiography which described the rigours of a Turkish childhood – spent largely at a school as bleak and brutal as Dotheboys Hall.) Looking only at their black smocks, one might take them for French schoolchildren of an earlier decade, who had stepped, perhaps, out of the pages of *Le Grand Meaulnes*. But their European appearance goes no further than their collars and cuffs: every third or fourth face bears in its features the unmistakeable impress of Asiatic Turkistan, and one or two of the children have brought musical instruments with them on the outing – swan-necked guitars bellying out into onion-shaped resonators like some Indian *vina* or *sita*. The boys are under the charge of two young ushers who see no purpose in dispensing instructional patter to their charges, and are content to relax on the grassy hump of the wall. (What is someone else's cultural heritage to them?) One thing alone sets them in motion: noticing June opening her camera, they elbow their way through the crowd of children, so as to be sure of being in the front of the picture.

Neither masters nor boys show any intention of entering the city proper, so we circumvent them and pass through the northeast gate. Ahead of us, the main street slopes gently upwards, between the foundations of long-lost villas and public buildings. Here and there, smaller side streets lead off at right angles, and just down one of these to the left we come into the *bouleuterion*, or council chamber. Here the echoes of the past are still almost audible: round three sides of a square, rows of stone seats rise one above another, facing the central altar. Poppy-seeds and grasses have lodged themselves in the crevices of the stone-work, but the whole structure – as neat, compact and well-preserved as the miniature stone theatre at Cos – could be reinstated at a day's notice.

Priene's own theatre is just the other side of the main street. Though larger than the theatre at Cos, it too is in good condition, and the seats of honour in the front row of the stalls still display the carved ivy-leaves of the city's symbol. At the far end of the main street, we come out onto the raised platform of the Temple of Athena. All that is left of the main structure is the scattered drums of fallen columns. But the situation of the Temple is as magnificent as ever: at the south-west corner, the hill falls away sheer to the lower half of the ruined town, and there we sit, sheltering ourselves from the wind behind the largest of the fluted drums, and waiting for Fotis to catch up with us. After a few minutes he puts in an appearance, tiptoeing in obvious agitation, and looking behind him into the grass: it is not usual to see him discomposed. 'Serpent,' he explains, grimacing and drawing in his broad shoulders, 'I saw a big serpent.'

After all these weeks, we are at last – literally – within sight of our journey's ultimate goal: the original birthplace of scientific speculation, Miletus. For it lies due south of Priene, eight miles away as the crow flies, across the Meander valley. Two thousand years ago and more, the view from this point would have carried the eye across the sparkling waters of the Gulf of Latmos to the headland beyond, where the fourfold harbours of Miletus sheltered behind a little group of islands; while, for another dozen miles further East, the deep inlet of the ancient bay would have stretched away (like the Ceramic Gulf at Cos) along the foot of the Five-Finger Mountains to the town of Heraklea. Now the head of the Gulf alone survives, to form an isolated inland lake, the Bafa Gölü. To the West, the encroaching silt of the Meander has converted the sea, first into a marsh, then into a fen, and by now into mile after mile of fruitful farmland – a full eight miles

174

separate the marshy fringe of the lake from the lagoons of the present-day Aegean coastline. Miletus itself stands half-way between them: although as late as A.D. 1350 its harbours were still open to shipping, something more than a dredger would be needed today to reopen the four miles of channel originally uniting it with the sea.

As things are, we look down from the ruined Temple of Athena onto the bare bones of an ancient shopping-street, which leads out at its western end into Priene's own lost harbour. Here the base of the Samsun Dag falls back to form a circular bay, open only to the South-east. In the days of Priene's glory, this was its port: now it is just one more field, with trim rows of olive-trees growing across and across it in geometrical order. We assemble the camera and tripod, pointing them down first at the harbour and then onto the fertile farmland of the delta beyond. Still gusting and violent, the wind tears at us as we work, threatening on occasion to capsize the tripod and plunge Fotis, camera and all, down over the edge onto the ruined houses below. Squatting between the tripod-legs, I clutch them firmly. Under June's direction, Fotis turns his attention to a line of poplars, which are dipping and swaying beside the bend of the river just below us; next, a little further right, to the rich fields of green tufted barley, across whose surface the *meltem* is driving wave after wave, like the swell out at sea; and finally – tilting the camera slowly up and to the right – across the five or six miles of newest land, to the low hills behind Miletus and the coastal lagoons, almost lost in the distant haze.

*   *   *

This was our fourth day in Turkey. In leaving Samos for Ionia, we had – inevitably – changed the focus of our investigations once again. For now we should be faced with an essential part of the *environment* of Greek science, yet one no longer occupied by an Hellenic people. (Presumably the influence of this environment could not, by itself, have imposed an Hellenic character upon its new, Turkish inhabitants.) We could not be happy to leave the Aegean without visiting the places where Thales,

Heraclitus, Anaxagoras, and the other founders of our intellectual tradition, lived and worked; yet we could bring to them only questions about their geographical character – the possibilities which, being what and where they were, these towns could have held out for intellectual life and development. What Greeks themselves could do in and with Ionia, it was too late to ask, for there are Greeks in Miletus and its sister-cities no longer.

We arrived equipped with one clue only – namely, the things Aristotle himself has to say about the origins of Ionian science. In the beginning, Aristotle insists, natural philosophy was not a practical art, like the medicine of Hippocrates or the engineering of Eupalinus: it was a purely theoretical matter, discussed for its own sake and without regard to practical utility:

When practically all the necessities of life were supplied, men turned to philosophy as a leisure-time recreation.

In some ways, this remark of Aristotle's was an odd one. Coming from a citizen of the barren limestone mainland, it had stuck in our minds; for how could all the necessities of life *ever* be supplied, in Greece of all places?

It was four in the morning when we had made ready to cast off from Tigani. Though the wind had gone down a lot, the weather was still heavy and lowering, with intermittent showers. On the quayside, as we pulled away, stood the damp and solitary figure of Robbie: he was due to return to Athens later in the day, on the regular steamer from Vathy. We motored out of the harbour, past Polycrates' mole, and on eastwards into the straits. By daylight, we were bucking around in the turgid race which runs between Samos and St Nicholas Island (Byrak Adasi), and being swept along by the current towards the Gulf of Kushadasi. Wooded hills dropped straight down to the sea on either side. A white maelstrom of cloud enveloped the lower spurs of the Samsun Dag. At times, the cloud dropped lower and thickened, deluging us with heavy rain; at times, it parted momentarily, revealing forested hillsides stretching upwards without visible limits. Soon the first rays of sunlight were skirting diagonally along the line of hills and slanting luminously through the cloud-layers, to spotlight the green of the trees clothing the eastward-facing shoulders of the range.

Once through the strait we made away in a north-easterly direction across the bay, while the shoreline fell back further to the East in a great arc. Gradually the sun established his ascendancy. As we pulled away northwards from the hill, the cloud lifted and lightened, to reveal a gentle rolling landscape broken by fields and trees, with something of the aspect of the Isle of Wight. A little hump on the flat coastline marked the site of an abandoned Venetian fort. A couple of miles further North, the land jutted out westwards again to meet us and we coasted along, taking care to keep outside the reefs which border Aslan Burnu (Lion Point) and Yalanci Burnu (Vine Point). Behind this double headland, the coast dropped back again, and we caught sight of a minute island topped by another medieval fort: this was the original Bird Island (Kush Adasi) from which our destination took its name. We rounded the point and the island beyond, and headed into the bay.

The port was unpromising. Two low-roofed factory buildings with chimneys, a scraggy mass of ancient fortifications, and a few dozen houses grouped along the shore and headland, one of them carrying the optimistic label 'Kasino' – that seemed to be all. Along the base of the bay was the older, and largely unprotected fishing-quay; while, at right angles to this, a new pier of formidable dimensions was in course of construction. Thick square concrete pillars thrust down into the sea-bed. The sides of the jetty were clad with sharp steel rods, plates and girders, and the sole means of getting from a dinghy onto the elevated platform of the main pier was a slippery concrete stairway devoid of handrail or other support. We contemplated this fearsome piece of engineering with a mixture of suspicion and respect. Given strong fenders, a full-sized ironclad steamer could no doubt have wharfed alongside it conveniently and comfortably; but as for a wooden sailing vessel less than fifty feet long, or a yacht's tender of barely nine . . . that was another matter.

There was about the pier something essentially un-maritime, non-functional. While the rough causeway thrown up to join

Bird Island to the shore near Vine Point would help somewhat to shelter the harbour from the South and West, the new pier would still (it was clear) leave no protection against the prevailing *meltem*. Driving in from the open Aegean between the island and the pier-head, the free-running swell would pour into the bay unchecked. Instead of serving the familiar needs of men long intimate with all the moods of the sea – instead of being designed by sailors, and for sailors – this jetty was a real landlubber of a construction. June and I grinned at one another, recalling the decrepit elevator at the Turkish Embassy in London: on our arrival, the porter had shown us briskly into it, clashed the gates to, and sent us clanking upwards before we had time to read the politely-phrased card fixed on the wall – 'Visitors are Warned that the Insurance Company has Declined to Accept any further Responsibility for this Lift'.

We came into the harbour with Stars and Stripes at the stern, and Dhaskalis' Turkish ensign at the yard-arm. A procession of officials formed up on the pier and, as soon as we were securely anchored, they filed down into a motor-boat and came across to us. We now discovered how efficiently Mr Wilkinson at Izmir had smoothed our path. Several times beforehand, we had been solemnly warned that, of all officials, Turkish officials were the most officious; and, arriving so soon after the military *coup d'état*, we were expecting the worst. Our fears were not borne out. Within twenty minutes all the formalities had been completed, and we were on our way across to the terrifying pier, taking with us rucksacks containing our immediate necessities.

Along with the party of officials was a young Turkish student who had an adequate working knowledge of English. He had been sent, he explained, to collect us and bring us to Izmir, where Mr Wilkinson was expecting us. His employer – he handed us a visiting card bearing the splendid name, *Ali Tashkent* – did many things for the British Consul-General: luckily, he had found a car for us to rent, so if we would just come with him. . . . We followed him along the inchoate jetty, picking our way round sacks of cement, steel reinforcing-rods, and a clutter of crowbars, planks and scaffolding. Beside the grass plots and ceremonial statue in the main square stood a brand-new Renault microbus. I made a mental note to ask about the hire-fee – Tom Crichton was in the middle of telling us something of his experiences with Turkish ship-chandlers – and murmured a provisional benediction on Ali Tashkent. To this we added a silent prayer that the *Jack London*, trapped in this rather dubious harbour, would come to no harm during our absence. She had a good stout anchor out, the rest of the ship's company were hardy and competent, so we could do nothing but accept the situation fatalistically. With a final *Mashallah*, we got on board the microbus and were swept away, June and I to conduct a preliminary reconnaissance, Tom to snatch a few days with a friend in Istanbul.

For three or four miles the road ran parallel to the coast, alternately climbing through olive-groves round the necks of headlands and dropping down to the shorelines of small bays. Third time round this cycle, we breasted a col from which a sudden panorama opened up. A broad estuarial plain, terminating in a beach like a golden bow, stretched away for some five or six miles to end in a line of low hills: across the middle of this plain flowed the norther, and lesser, of the two Meander Rivers. The road turned inland, and began to drop gradually to the level of the plain.

After everything we had accustomed ourselves to in Greece and the Islands, this Ionian landscape struck us with a downright physical impact. We sat up: here was something completely new. The first thing to impress us was the profusion of Nature. Drifts of wild flowers – red, white and purple – were scattered innumerable across the verges and pastures. Then, more significant, we remarked on the depth and richness of the farmland: here, instead of localized pockets of fertility confined between barren limestone hills, there were thousands of acres of thick alluvial soil, continually renewed and extended by the generosity of the broad river. Yet, as we ran up the Meander Valley, the thing that finally impressed us most was the new character which the river-valley gave to the landscape. For this was no short-run affair, no mountain torrent falling steeply off the hills and irrigating a narrow plain, only to disappear into the sea. This was the seaward end of a true continental river – short, maybe, when compared with the Greater Meander of Miletus, or the Gediz further North, but flowing in the same leisurely way down a broad and slowly-falling trough. From where we entered its valley, above the very mouth of the river, our eyes were at once carried far inland. Indeed, the whole aspect of the landscape had something Continental about it: the uplands of Anatolia, and the great land-mass of Asia itself, were already making their presence felt. After a few miles we had lost even the smell of the sea, and were adapting ourselves to a new land-horizon.

We joined the main road at Seljuk, just past the side-turning to Efes, the site of ancient Ephesus. On the left, overlooking the town, stood a great rambling ruin of russet brick – the last skeleton of the sixth-century basilica, built by the Emperor Justinian over the tomb of St John the Apostle, and surrounded by the walls of the Byzantine citadel. Under the mound on which it stood, houses and shops clustered together round the main cross-roads, and the vast brushwood porcupines of storks' nests on the shallow-pitched tile roofs tipped and trembled as their ungainly occupants teetered upon them. Here we turned north again, leaving behind the frog-filled marsh of the delta with its embroidery of giant yellow cow-parsley, and running along past the first lush orchards of Smyrna figs. June was looking meditatively out of the window of the car.

'H'm, Aristotle,' she murmured: 'you can see what Aristotle meant *here*.'

'Yes,' I agreed, ' "When all the wants of man were supplied. ..." The Ionians certainly had a good start.'

Now the first strings of camels were appearing: some of them plodding and swaying gently along, four or five to a string, others lying at the roadside and resting their packs on the grass verge. Storks, camels, big orchards, alluvial valleys: all these novel features of Ionia conspired to make Aristotle's verdict on the origins of science appear less eccentric. Given a few acres of olives, figs and vines, it was at any rate no longer *inconceivable* that men should have had the freedom, the energy and the leisure to sit around and philosophize for the first time. Certainly, we still had some questions to answer. By itself, *opportunity* could hardly be the whole story. It might explain one thing: how the new philosophical discussion, having once germinated, could grow and flourish, instead of being stillborn. But, to set the discussion going in the first place, there must have been some additional *stimulus*, and the natural wealth of the Ionian farmland alone could not explain what this stimulus was. Again: the scientific speculations of the first Ionians were concentrated in Miletus, and why (we should have to ask) should Miletus have proved a favourable soil for the new intellectual growth while – so far as we know – Priene, just across the bay, contributed nothing?

From Ephesus to Izmir took us not much more than an hour. Once through the first suburbs of the city, packed with bicycles and hand-carts, we crested the final col and dipped into a zig-zag descent towards the centre of the town. Ahead of us was the great inlet of the Gulf of Izmir: below us, the conglomeration of tiled roofs was fringed by a line of docks and boulevards, and dotted with minarets. Down to the waterfront, past the main port, and along the promenade. . . . We pulled up sharply, beside a flight of stone steps and heavy, varnished double-doors. We had arrived.

May 2. The Consulate-General preserves untouched the diplomatic life of fifty years ago. Superb atmosphere of hush: relaxing club furniture and lace curtaining. The Consul-General himself – trim, compact, well-proportioned, dark-suited, clean-scrubbed. ' . . . Some corner of a foreign field – That is for ever Whitehall. . . .' But if only the Home Civil still had time to cope with one's every last problem, as he has done! Self-invited, unimportant, we are made to feel like Royalty – but then, perhaps academics *are* a pleasant change, after penniless hitch-hikers, V.I.Ps. and Ambassadors (the three chief *bêtes-noires* of a Consul's life in that order) In fact, W. is a talented and well-informed classical archaeologist, knowing his territory as only a good Consul-General (permanently resident) is able to do.

He confirms our impressions about the natural wealth of Ionia: 'Under the Roman Empire, you know, Western Turkey alone probably had a population of twenty-five million – as many as the whole country today.' The camels? He tells how a coachload of English tourists ('Yes, the conducted tours have reached us even here, I'm afraid') set off from Izmir for Ephesus: 'When they passed the first train of camels, one elderly woman begged the coach-driver to stop, so that she might photograph them. Having got down on to the verge, she could not be persuaded to re-embark. Her chief hope in coming all this way, she said, had been to see camels in their natural habitat; and, having reached her goal, she was not going to be separated from them the very next moment. Let the rest of the coachload go on to Ephesus – she didn't want to see a lot of ruins, she would stay here with the camels. It took a lot of doing to make her realize the camels were only resting, and would soon be moving on . . . she wanted to stay with them, and accompany them wherever they went. The guides could get her back again into the coach only forcibly and under protest.'

W. says that the authorities are still touchy after the army revolution, and we shall have to watch our step. It was a good thing we steered clear of Cnidus: if we'd gone too close, the coastguards would cheerfully have shot at us, and if we'd set foot ashore he'd have been having to get us out of prison. Quite a lot of the country still consists of 'military areas'; and we shall certainly need the Letters of Authority from Ankara which are waiting for us at the local broadcasting station. Quite apart from the military areas, we may have difficulty in photographing people, especially women. Freya Stark gets away with it; but then she is over seventy and, what with all her patent camping equipment and everything, the locals consider her 'a bit mad', and are specially tolerant. (This reputation for lunacy is one of which English travellers down the centuries have had the sense to take full advantage.)

Smyrna figs: I had forgotten about the English connection. Passing the time of day, June inquires which are the fashionable parts of Izmir – where does the élite (meaning the top Turks) of Izmir live? W's answer rings a bell in my mind: 'Oh, mainly in Buca and Bornova – the Whittalls particularly have always lived at Bornova.' The Whittalls? Why of course: like the wine-trade from Oporto, the fig-trade from Smyrna was for more than a century the preserve of English dynasties, who settled here and soon ruled the roost. Even the local wild tulip is called *Tulipa Whittallii*, having been collected and introduced to cultivation by Edward Whittall, one of the dynasty. 'But of course,' adds W. sadly, 'there's not the same opportunity for the English here now, and there aren't many Whittalls left. Nearly all the younger ones have gone – mostly to Southern Rhodesia, I believe....'

Ali Tashkent ('A good fellow, Ali Bey,' says W. 'He found this car for you, quite a bargain I believe – and he can fix you up with anything else you want.') is a very different figure: squat, square, like granite, tiny office upstairs off a back street. Old Levant can out-bargain modern New York any day of the week. Civilities, a wave of the hand – to fetch coffee – tramping of underlings, protracted tele-phone calls. Each new visitor displays Ali Bey in a fresh guise: 'Excuse me a moment, I have to send these men to pack some furniture for CENTO.' – 'Ah yes, I am very busy: later in the month I go to Istanbul to meet *Britannia*' – 'You see the blue streak in this piece of rock? That I am sure is turquoise. It comes from Samsun Dag, near where you are going: I have spent eleven million Turkish pounds on prospecting for minerals, and I must get an expert opinion. Do you think this could be arranged in England?' After coffee, we come round to the question of the hired car. Fortunately we have now joined up with Michael, our interpreter. (Delicate negotiations are easier in Turkish.) The asking price is on the high side, so we haggle – in a gentlemanly way, of course. Toing and froing; the owner of the car is called in; but honour is finally satisfied all round. We are to pay between four and five pounds sterling a day, but this is to include unlimited mileage, plus the service of *two* full-time assistants – driver and guide. We shake Ali Bey's rugged hand, expressing infinite indebtedness, and retire down the wooden stairway and out to the street.

Mr Wilkinson had whetted our appetite: the terms of the car contract made up our minds. Mileage was no longer any object. We would send for Fotis and the cameras in the morning, and make inland from Izmir at least as far as Sardis. There were other Ionian cities near at hand, also: notably Clazomenae and Teos, on either side of the promontory to the west of Izmir. For the moment, there was little more we could usefully do: we signed in at the Izmir Palas Hotel, and dismissed the car for the night. The immediate neighbourhood was more easily explored either on foot, or in one of the Ruritanian horse-carriages which were clip-clopping slowly up and down the avenues between the Kulturpark and the waterfront.

Later: We visit the International Fair buildings in the Kulturpark: Universal Exhibition style. One of them (Michael tells us) announces itself as a Pavilion of Folk-Handicrafts – surely we shall find here some antique Turkish silver? Ghastly disappointment: lots of plastic and cheap mass-produced glassware. One stall of horn-clad penknives, one with some pleasant gilded liqueur-glasses and coffee-cups, otherwise uniform shoddiness throughout. Finally on the top floor, we run to earth one stall displaying some silver – nothing more than a pair of Victorian egg-cups and two things looking like christening-mugs. Nothing exciting, but it seems worth inquiring about prices. The girl behind the stall tinkles with laughter. 'They're not *for sale*,' she explains: 'they're only on show – so as to demonstrate how this old stuff can be improved by *nickel-plating*.'

Fortunately the new (and drab) had not entirely smothered the old (but despised). Next day, while waiting for Fotis, we go exploring in the bazaar, where the traditional crafts and manners of life have not yet finally surrendered. Here a street of coppersmiths makes finely-decorated jugs and bowls, there a dozen pewter-workers are turning out identical teapots. Another street is all spices and herbs, or fruits, or fabrics; while finally, returning under Michael's guidance, we locate the street of the silversmiths, and thankfully find that the old standards of work have not wholly vanished.

By lunchtime, however, Fotis and Helen have arrived, and it is time to reconnoitre further.

May 3, *p.m.* Clazomenae, otherwise Urla Iskelesi: piety compels us to visit Anaxagoras' native town, twenty miles along the south shore of the Gulf of Izmir. As merchants and seamen, the men of Clazomenae competed with the Phoenicians right up to the time of the Persian invasion. After the conquest by Cyrus in 546 B.C. they retired to a small island a quarter of a mile off the coast, and it was presumably there that Anaxagoras was born some fifty years later. Like so many of the Greek towns along this coastline, Clazomenae was forced always to defend its independence against someone – the Lydians from Sardis, or the Persians, or the mainland Greeks, or the Macedonians. They were finally engulfed by the armies of Alexander the Great, and the causeway joining the island to the shore dates from his time.

In her book on *Ionia*, Freya Stark mused at Clazomenae to particularly good purpose. But really: for once her romantic imagination surely overreached itself! Urla Iskelesi is an undistinguished fishing hamlet, comparable to (say) Bradwell-on-Sea. The curved stone jetty is distinguished only by an antique Ottoman sentry-box at the far end; half-a-dozen houses along the waterfront sleep out the afternoon, with the air of some ramshackle one-horse town in a Western; Alexander's causeway is still there, but Anaxagoras' native island has become a quarantine hospital.

We drive back through the cornfields and five miles along the main road towards Izmir; then down through a land of oaks and parkland, followed by open heath, to Seferihisar and Sigacik, next to the ancient Teos. The village is again in siesta, but it has a character wholly lacking at Urla. The square walls of the Genoese fortress are still largely in place, forming a kind of miniature Aigues-Mortes. The winding inlets from the sea have something in common with the upper reaches of Milford Haven. Even Freya Stark could find at Sigacik little more than a couple of pieces of archaic masonry under a nearby hedge; all in all, Sigacik tells us more about Miletus than it does about Teos. For the layout – with multiple harbours sheltering on either side of a headland – provides some idea of what Miletus must have been before the silt of the Greater Meander finally overwhelmed its harbours.

The afternoon is grey and chilly. Within the walls, the streets of the village are all mud and hen-droppings: half-a-dozen fishermen are standing around by a café, just outside the fortifications. The oldest of them, bald-headed with grey-knitted pullover and jolly European face, offers us glasses of tea. (The homegrown Turkish tea is excellent.) Michael draws our attention to their features: Central Asian features are evident in perhaps a quarter of these 'Turkish' countryfolk. 'They're really Hittites,' he declares. Even 'though they think of themselves as Turks, the Asiatic invasions can never have done more than dilute the original prehistoric stock. The ancestors of these farmers and fishermen have been here ever since 1500 B.C. – probably longer.' We drink the little glasses of milkless tea thankfully, and make our farewells. '*Güle, güle* – laughingly, laughingly': the salutation is deprecatory, an isolated fragment torn from an embroidered fabric of formalities – 'No offence taken, I'm sure.' There is something over-drilled about it, something which sets the Turks alongside the English and the Japanese, and divides them utterly from the Greeks, with their unaffected and direct '*Chairete* – Be happy'.

This first brief excursion from Izmir added little to our previous picture of the Ionian colonies – that string of independent ports and trading-stations scattered along the Aegean coastline of Asia Minor and bound together, at most, into loose political confederations. In order to add some depth to our impressions, it was desirable to go further inland. So first thing next morning we were back in the little bus, and picking our way against the stream of commuter-traffic (carts and bicycles outnumbering cars), through the eastern quarters of Izmir, past the Whittall's garden-suburb of Bornova, and into the open country. Muslim Orthodoxy has relaxed enough to permit the planting of vineyards, and the valley of Kavaklidere gives its name to a pleasant light dinner-wine. After a few miles the road zig-zags out of the plain and up to a low pass. We stop to photograph the innocent countryside, but are pounced on by a young man who announces himself as the local mayor: this, he declares, is a 'military area', and he is grudgingly pacified only by Michael and the precious letters from Ankara.

We cross the pass, and the valley of the Gediz opens before us. Sardis, our destination, is sixty miles East of Izmir, and half-way up towards the Anatolian plateau. This new valley is twice as wide as that of the Lesser Meander, and correspondingly more fertile. To the left, the river bends away slightly North-west, before turning west again to meet the sea south of Pergamon, near the ancient Phocaea. (What an enduring mark these coastal cities were to leave on the subsequent history and life of Europe! All over Europe, the bleached goatskins from Pergamon became known as *parchment*; while from Phocaea came the colonists who founded Marseilles, and by another single step reached as far as the tin-mines of Cornwall.)

Ten miles away, to the North of the river, a long grey line of hills was ruled along the horizon towards the East. We dropped down the river, and turned up the valley. Driving inland, our earlier impressions were confirmed and reinforced. Here was a country of great natural wealth: one which could support more than its present population, even with primitive methods of cultivation. The expulsion of the Greeks in the early 1920s closed an historical episode more than 3,000 years old; but it did so tragically and needlessly – it was one more bitter fruit of that petty nationalism by which the twentieth century has been cursed.

Yet now this first impression was joined by a second. For at this point we were entering the territory of ancient Lydia – the country which, in the eyes of the classical Greeks, was luxurious above all others – the country of Croesus, proverbially the richest man in the world. The fertile valley through which we were driving could doubtless have supplied all the food and cloth the Lydians needed for a self-sufficient existence; but their reputation for fabulous wealth must have been built on something more than figs and goatskins.

As the microbus ran smoothly up the newly-surfaced road, it was not hard to appreciate what this extra something was. For we were now on the main highway to 'the East', Sardis was not just the chief market-town of a prosperous agricultural zone: it was the focal-point onto which the trade-routes from Persia, Syria and Mesopotamia converged as they dropped down from Anatolia into the coastal valleys. So long as the Lydians held Sardis and the adjoining valleys, they could exact a tithe of the commerce coming overland from Asia to the Aegean. And, though Croesus' kingdom and riches were destroyed by the invasion of Cyrus the Great soon after 550 B.C., Sardis kept its importance as a provincial capital within the Persian Empire. (The famous Royal Road, from Persepolis and Susa to the Greek lands, terminated here.) For many centuries, indeed – up to Byzantine times and later – the effective boundary between Asia and Europe ran, not along the coastline, but rather through Sardis.

Figs, vines, grain, sheep, goats, locust-beans, with here and there the white poppies of an opium field: the high road drove on Eastwards up the lush valley. Here a turbaned farmer, with brown leathery face, leant on his hoe, stroking his drooping moustaches. There a line of women, in veils and bloomers, squatted as they set the young tobacco plants into rough trenches. Across the valley on a low plain overlooking the river, a group of low grass-

187

covered domes came in sight – the enormous barrows which survive from the burial-grounds of the ancient Kings of Lydia.

At Sardis itself, nothing remains which one can confidently date back to Lydian times. But even now the great Temple of Artemis, rebuilt on the orders of Alexander the Great about 330 B.C., preserves traces of that oriental splendour and magnificence which the Greeks associated with Lydia and Croesus. The northern quarter of the city spanned the main highway, but the centre of the town lay up a side valley (known to the Greeks as the Pactolus) and was provided with a natural defence by a ring of precipitous hills. Here, on a piece of flat land above the stream, Alexander's Artemision overlays the remains of Croesus' own temple. At the West end, a pair of soaring columns still stands, and beside their elaborately-decorated bases lies the wreckage of several others. Nearer the road, one can see the ruins of a Roman or Byzantine gateway, but the centre of the deserted city is covered over by the farmhouses and sheep-pens of modern Sert: the glory of Croesus has finally departed.

May 4. Lunch at Salihli, six miles on from Sardis. Grubby market town with a population of nine thousand. Pastry-shop-cum-restaurant: a crowded dining-room rather than a *taverna*, with farmers in cloth caps and earth-dusty suits. Stuffed vine-leaves, meat-balls, artichokes, yoghourt, with *baclava* and glasses of tea to follow. June and Helen very much exceptions. Here inland the emancipation of woman has far to go. The *patron* keeps his wife in an unlit kitchen behind the dining-room, concealed by a curtain of sacking. He thrusts dirty plates through a gap in the curtain, and takes back newly-washed glasses and cutlery in exchange. Once or twice, we catch a female eye peeping (? enviously) through a gap in the sacking.

The upland road over Böz Dag is declared impassable, and this compels a change of plan. (Yes, confirmed Mr Wilkinson later: it had taken him two days to make the crossing in his own car, after flash-floods the previous autumn.) So much for our hopes of a round-trip ending up at Kushadasi – there is nothing for it but to return the same way.

By the time we got back to the Meander Valley it was evening. We drove into Seljuk in the dark and the rain, with a blustery wind blowing up from the West. What hope was there of getting back on board the *Jack London* tonight – to say nothing of getting a meal when we did? What point, indeed, was there in *trying* to do so? We unloaded from the bus and pushed our way into a crowded restaurant. All the farmers of the region – we guessed – must be gathered together and compressed into a single room, and once again June and Helen were the only women present. Our fellow-diners were tanned, creased, relaxed – yet somehow introverted. There was none of the familiar Greek ebullience: they were content (it seemed) because they were undemanding, and lived within a known framework of conventions. A space was made for us at one of the back tables. The menu provided for bread, wine and the usual variations on lamb, rice and yoghourt. We were received with politeness, but without curiosity. Placed in the same position in a Greek town, we should have been bombarded with personal questions: the men of Seljuk kept themselves to themselves. One man alone, marked out from the others by a metropolitan air and a green tweed jacket, acknowledged the presence of visitors, ordering the *patron* – with a courtly gesture – to bring us a second bottle of wine.

When we arrived back at Kushadasi, Helen and June voted unhesitatingly against attempting the boat-trip to the *J.L.* in the dark; and even the second-hand sheets and penetrating urinal-smell of the local hotel (ill-named the *Palas*) could not change their minds. Fotis, however, had been separated from Maureen for too long and went off in search of a boatman, promising to be ashore again early next day for the trip down to Priene and Miletus. We retired to our 'palace', and found with relief that the local police had insisted – on their own initiative – that the dirty sheets be removed. Rolling ourselves in jerseys and blankets, we slept as well as the prevailing odours and the squeaking chain-mail under the lumpy mattresses permitted. It was a night to forget: when morning came, we set off happily, bumping along an earth road over the headland to the south of Kushadasi, and down to the little cultivated plain beyond.

Seen in the clean morning light, this corner of the country had something idyllic about it. Here the northern offshoots of the

Samsun Dag formed an arena of low hills, and along the small streams which ran down from the hills to the sea lines of vivid green showed where the poplars were coming into new leaf. The spring ploughing was in progress: yoked together in pairs, heavy white oxen trudged up and down the dusty fields, hauling simple wooden-framed ploughs. The road climbed windingly up the first of the foothills, then tilted over the watershed and ran downwards again along a broom-covered hillside: the grass verges were dotted with wild flowers, and the shrubs were bursting into the first sprays of white and yellow. Reaching the foot of this side-valley, we came out into Söke, at the edge of the Greater Meander plain. A horse-market was in progress. We picked our way carefully through the crowds, crossed a hump-backed bridge, and turned South-west along the foot of the hills towards Priene.

*　　*　　*

The natural processes which, over the centuries, have left Priene and Miletus stranded miles inland are still going on. The Mecca of our whole journey lies visible across the delta from Priene; yet the signposts for 'Balat' (as Miletus is now called) quite contradict both our Admiralty charts and the maps in the *Guide Bleu*, by pointing us still further south-westwards along a rough track towards the sea. On balance, the signposts appear more likely to be trustworthy, so we follow the track along the lower slopes of the Samsun Dag as far as the village of Dumuz Köy. Here we stop at a general-store full of candles, kerosene, grain-seed and sandpaper, to buy enough coarse bread, cheese and olives for our lunch.

At this point, we are on the very fringe of the coastal lagoons, and the track turns through a right-angle away from the hills, cutting straight across the rough marshland towards the small hills beside Miletus. (Once upon a time, these humps formed the off-shore island of Lade, rising out of the sea to a conical peak 330 feet high; and behind them the ships of Miletus found shelter from the *meltem*.) Half-way across the delta, we discover just *why* the road from Priene has been diverted: the Meander river has entirely changed its course, for at least the hundredth time. Both map and guide-book show the river as skirting Miletus and cutting down to the sea behind the Lade hills, but now it crosses under our road well to the North of Lade, and some four miles from the site of Miletus.

We pause by the river, content to defer the moment of fulfilment. Upstream, the rough riverside pastures are slowly losing their salinity, and they are now sweet enough for the sheep to graze them. Downstream, the newly-forming land is still given over to reeds and sea-birds. The silt-laden river has the texture of brown soup and, where the reeds come to an end at the water's edge, the wavelets lapping at their feet deposit every day their fresh donations of tilth. In the great cycle of creation by which, as it seemed to the Ionians, all things were carried round in an eternal flux, there was visible evidence here to demonstrate one essential link: namely, the transformation of water into earth. As devout pilgrims, we allowed ourselves one piece of self-indulgence, and imagined how Thales himself might have lectured beside this very river, and pointed out to his audience the process we were now watching as confirming the unlimited versatility of Water.

The doctrine that even the solidest of substances are composed in the last resort of Water, was never ridiculous; and it was conclusively undermined less than 200 years ago. When Thales took over from the traditional mythologies the conception of Water as the underlying matter of all things, he established a theoretical tradition that remained alive right up to the eighteenth century A.D. Its most notable modern advocates were to be the seventeenth-century Flemish physician, J. B. van Helmont, and the English gentleman-scientist, Robert Boyle. Van Helmont saw the forms and characters of material things as imposed on the universal, characterless Water which they incorporated, by the agency of certain inborn organizing powers which varied from one species of creature to another. Robert Boyle, though usually sceptical about all such general theories, shared van Helmont's belief that Water was infinitely transformable: indeed, he believed that he could demonstrate it changing progressively into solid form, if heated for a long time in a glass beaker. It was left to Lavoisier, a century later, to complete Boyle's own sceptical demolition-work, by repeating his experiments and establishing that the 'solid fragments' so produced were in fact only fragments of glass which had flaked off and broken away from the inside of the flask. In this way, a crucial link in the Ionians' cycle of trans-formations was finally broken, and one of the road-blocks was removed from the path of Lavoisier's own new chemical theory.

Having filmed the silting-process, we lean on the parapet of the bridge, masticating the pleasantly sour bread and crumbly cheese, and spitting olive-pips into the river. There is a soft thudding on the grass verge, as a farmer canters up on his horse: he reins in for a moment, scrutinizing us silently, then clatters on over the timbers of the bridge and away across the pastures. His sudden appearance imports a momentary flavour of the Central Asian steppes into the lonely marshlands of the delta. For the Turkish horseman is still (so to say) like a penguin: put down on his own two feet, he stumps about bow-legged and clumsy, but set where he is at home – in the saddle – he will swoop and curve with all the dash and beauty of a bird in flight. Knees pressed well in, and cloth cap pulled down over his eyes, the rider arrows his way across the fields towards Miletus.

We pack the last of our equipment back into the van and move off, rounding the landward end of the Lade Hills and crossing the empty channel of the old river before turning left into the ruins. Like some Imperial forerunner of the Sydney Opera House, the vast shell of the Roman theatre overshadows everything else. Standing here in the middle of open country, with nothing but farmhouses to give it scale, it looks as large as the Wembley Stadium; and indeed, its soaring tiers provided seating for an audience of 25,000. It took more than the tides of human politics to kill Miletus. Persians, Macedonians, Romans, Byzantines, Arabs, Turks: in the fourteenth century, the Venetians still knew Miletus as an active commercial port and built their own church in the city. In terms of sheer prosperity, indeed, Miletus reached its peak in Roman times, long after the days of the philosophers,

and this stranded whale of a theatre was built around the year
A.D. 200, when Thales had been dead for 700 years. Even then
the life of the city was only half-run. Miletus remained one of the
chief ports in the Roman Province of Asia – one of the wealthiest
parts of the Empire – and the bulky wreckage of Imperial
Miletus buried completely the last traces of Thales' native town.

We can soon see that what is left of Miletus offers the camera
nothing which would be relevant for our quest. It is a Mecca
without a Kaaba, a Rome without a St Peter's. As the afternoon is
far along, we ask after a lodging for the night. Balat itself consists of the few scattered houses which survived the earthquake of
1955, but a passing countryman directs us up the road to Yeni
(New) Balat and Akköy. The first of these looks like an English
suburban housing-estate, the second is a broken-down stone
hamlet still showing the scars of the earthquake. Michael gets
down from the bus, and tries to get some response from the
villagers. Blank cold faces convey not hostility but absolute in-
difference, *je-m'en-foutisme*, couldn't-care-lessery. (At a certain,
desperate level of sub-subsistence, people even lose interest in
taking your money; though once again – surely – even the
poorest Greeks would have been stirred by motives of hospitality,
or at any rate curiosity!) There is no choice: we shall find no
bed this side of Söke. Turning the car in the market-place, we
start the bumpy drive back down the two miles of dusty track
through the foothills to Miletus. At the river bridge beyond the
town, we pause once more. It is the end of the day and, away to the
North-west, the orange disc of the sun stands poised above the
silhouette of Samos, preparing for its plunge below the horizon.
In the evening light, the coastal marshes glow olive-green, while
the river itself flows like molten copper towards the Western sea.
As deserted as Jamestown, or like some archaic Rye, the birthplace of scientific theory sleeps under an orange haze.

*　　*　　*

Was the final goal of our whole journey to be a complete anti-
climax? Despite all our frustrated hopes and anticipations, it did

not seem that way. After all, what brought us to Miletus was no mere 'petrolatry': to have been shown Thales' tombstone would have added little to our experience. The scale and location of the town told us far more than fragments of masonry could do, and by now the lessons we had learned from the expedition were falling into a pattern.

'When nearly all the necessities of life were supplied, men turned to philosophy as a leisure-time recreation.' So said Aristotle; and that was one important element in the situation. By now, however, we could see some other relevant factors, and the outlines of the overall picture were crisper and clearer. To begin with: Aristotle's 'necessities of life' covered more than food, clothing and the like. Give men the richest farmlands in the world, and they will still have too little energy left at the end of the day for abstract, theoretical discussions. To find an agricultural society of high intellect and culture, one has to look (say) to the Southern States of the USA, in the generations before the Civil War; and there, the leisure of the landowners was paid for by the labour of their slaves. So far as we know, however, the Greek communities along the Ionian coastline were egalitarian societies. No: the leisure Aristotle pointed to as a necessary condition for the birth of philosophy was the product, not of agriculture alone, but of commerce. Heraclitus' Ephesus, Xenophanes' Colophon, and Anaxagoras' Clazomenae: these were all active trading-centres, as were Eudoxus' Cnidus, and the Miletus of Thales, Anaximander and Anaximenes.

Yet this, too, is only part of the story. Economic conditions may prepare a seedbed for new ideas: they do not by themselves *create* them. This remarkable group of men, having the leisure and energy not only to initiate a scientific and philosophical debate, but to sustain it over several generations, was without question a symptom of the economic vigour of the Ionian trading-ports. (In this, Thales and his successors remind one of eighteenth-century Birmingham's Lunar Society.) But what was the seed from which sprang the new, critical attitudes of mind so character-istic of Greek philosophy?

About this, Freya Stark had given us a hint which both fitted well into our picture of the Ionian ports and would apply equally to the Greek towns of Southern Italy – the region to which Pythagoras successfully transplanted the philosophical debate. These communities were not only active, prosperous, independent, individualistic city-states: they were also *frontier* towns. In the end, this frontier position was their undoing. The boundary between the Aegean and Middle Eastern worlds was maintained only by a delicate balance of power, which the Persian Wars upset; and, as the coastal towns lost their independence, the cultural centre of the Greek world moved West across the Aegean to the rising city of Athens. Yet for some 200 years, in a world which was ready to move on from the ideological clamour of rival mythologies, Clazomenae, Colophon, Ephesus and Miletus occupied a crucial position. In a dozen ways, their lives and their trade compelled them to recognize the contrasts between the conventions and beliefs of different civilizations.

This, surely – as Freya Stark suggests – is the significance of Xenophanes' pioneer excursion into comparative religion. The traditional imagery of the different national religions (he saw) had something absurd about it: men always ended by modelling their gods on themselves. Homer and Hesiod had attributed to the gods all the vices of human beings, and the various nations of the world depicted their deities with all their own racial peculiarities:

The Ethiopians make their gods black and snub-nosed; the Thracians say theirs have blue eyes and red hair. . . . Yes, and if oxen and horses or lions had hands, and could paint with their hands, and could produce works of art as men do, horses would paint the forms of the gods like horses, and oxen like oxen, and make their bodies in the image of their several kinds.

This was radical talk, yet Xenophanes was no atheist. Rather he was a pioneer monotheist, anxious to go behind the multiplicity of traditional divinities to a supreme underlying power, and to identify this unique God with the creative force in Nature. All the same, in the more conservative atmosphere of Thebes or Babylon, such an argument would have sounded blasphemous.

For Egypt and Mesopotamia had always been central powers: self-sufficient countries, whose prosperity depended on a coherent and stable social system. Both civilizations had grown from the battle to win command over great rivers, and in each culture established cycles of ritual and belief preserved a way of life built up painfully over 3,000 years. Individual Egyptians and Babylonians may have recognized that their own mythologies were not unique; but any stirring of scepticism they felt could scarcely have become at all general – even if (remembering the fate of the heretical Pharaoh Ikhnaton) it were safe to express them openly.

The very special position of the Ionian towns was to be reproduced in part 2,000 years later, in Venice, Padua and the other independent city-states of Northern Italy. As a result of their commerce the Venetians knew, as few of their contemporaries did, just how rich and various were all the different human races, societies, and religions. In name, of course, they were spiritually subject to the centralizing authority of Rome; but they were rich enough, and distant enough from the Vatican, to value their independence – both in political and in ideological affairs. This frontier position was reinforced when the Reformation swept northern Europe, converting much of Germany into a rival ideological focus: thereafter the Republic of Venice could always blackmail the Romans with the threat of a German Alliance – rather as the Ionians played off the mainland Greeks against the Lydians and the Persians. In Rome itself, the dice were naturally loaded against radical and unorthodox speculations: in Padua and Venice, they had a better chance of being considered on their merits. Indeed, if Galileo had been teaching not in the North, but at Rome, he would have got into serious trouble (one suspects) a great deal sooner than he did. And Galileo had his counterpart in the classical era: doctrines which Anaxagoras had taught with impunity in Ionia (e.g. that the sun is a lump of flaming rock) led him later at Athens into being denounced for impiety.

The Ionians took over the subject-matter of their speculations from Egypt and Mesopotamia: it was in their attitudes and methods of thought that they were originators and pioneers. Thales, Pythagoras and Eudoxus all reputedly visited one or other of the older civilizations, and studied the mathematical and astronomical traditions handed down by the priesthoods of the great Middle Eastern Empires. Yet, significantly, these visitors from the Aegean coastline were able to give a new twist to these older traditions, snapping the threads which had joined them to the national mythologies of their birthlands. So it was in the Greek cities of Ionia, where a new freedom from the constraints of conservatism allowed the stimulus of cross-cultural contacts full play, that the Wisdom of the East – then, as now, religious in its affiliations – was transformed, budding off a novel offshoot: the rational, critical, speculative tradition of Greek science and philosophy.

Asia Minor, then, was the placenta, and the cities of Ionia the umbilical cord, by which the new Hellenic civilization on the shores of the Mediterranean drew nourishment from the older land-borne societies of the Middle East. The first serious threat to this organic connection came from the Arabs in the seventh century A.D., and the arrival of the Turks four centuries later largely destroyed it. As Europe grew to maturity and independence, the vital functions of this connection had in any case lost their importance; and, since the flight of the remaining Greek farmers and merchants in the 1920s, the separation of Europe and Asia has at this point become complete. The Ionian cities lie ruined and deserted, with no more significance than a withered navel-string.

In the land where Greek science was born, the life and traditions are now entirely Turkish; and though, during the great years of the Ottoman Empire, some sort of a naval tradition was grafted onto earlier Turkish ways of life, the graft never took very well. In their dealings with the sea, the Turks had never acquired the finesse that comes from an intimate and harmonious experience. The rough clumsiness that we had remarked on in the pier at Kushadasi was evident again in the design of the fishing-boats tied up along the quay at Izmir: there was something almost medieval about their shape, like the galleys in some fifteenth-

197

century painting – as though someone was only just getting around to inventing the stern-post rudder.

The Greeks themselves are very conscious of this contrast between the Turkish traditions and their own. They tell with unkind relish of the Turkish admiral sent from Istanbul to take part in the celebrations at Malta on the occasion of Queen Victoria's Jubilee. One day out from home, he called in at an Aegean island, and telegraphed back, 'Where is Malta?' A few days later, he wired from Crete for further instructions: 'Cannot find Malta.' He spent the next week cruising vaguely around in the Central Mediterranean, then turned up at Crete again and sent his superiors a final laconic cable. This read simply: '*Malta yok* – there is no Malta.' And, though this story may be a wild exaggeration, it remains true that Turkish habits of life and thought face inland and eastwards, looking back to the vast plains and plateaux of Asia. However far (as Michael had said) the peasants of Anatolia are of local Hittite stock rather than Mongols from Turkestan, they have long since taken over and assimilated the attitudes and ideals of their Turkish conquerors.

To the founders of their own Asiatic culture, the Greeks and Byzantines of Constantinople and the coastal cities were a pack of unbelievers, whose monuments and institutions were something to be taken over or destroyed; and the wreckage of these earlier civilizations still possess little significance for their successors in Turkey today. As a result, twentieth-century Ionia has the air of a stately English home taken over as war-time billets for the boys of a public school; and this impression is reinforced by the formalized ethos, and introversion of personality, which so mark off the Turks from the Greeks. (Like the British public-school code and manner, these are the desiccated end-products of an Empire which, in its own time, was as dominant as the British Empire, even if less far-flung.)

Yet the country and history of Ionia are beginning to impose their character even onto these very different Turkish traditions. Our work at Priene and Miletus was complete, and it was time to catch up with our cultural obligations. So next afternoon we at last got around to visiting the ruins of Ephesus. For most of

198

the year, the women of the countryside are kept hard at work on their farm. ('I would rather be a cow here than a woman,' June had decided: 'at any rate the cows sometimes have the chance of a rest.') But this was the Saturday of the Spring *Bairam*. For one day – it being a festival of fertility – the women of the countryside were given leave from the fields, and moved about freely and unveiled in the Bank Holiday crowd. Ever since early morning the farmers and their families had been converging onto the ancient city of Ephesus. Coming over the hill after breakfast, on our return from Söke to Kushadasi, June and I had stopped at the head of a valley leading to Panionium and the foot of Mount Mycale; and as we worked by the roadside, a gaily coloured cart rattled by, carrying a whole family down to the festivities, dressed in their holiday best. Now at lunch-time, after a morning's work filming a string of camels, we parked the Renault at the entrance to the ruins and plunged into the mêlée.

There were seven of us – June, Helen and myself, the two young Turks, Michael, and a slightly grumpy Fotis. (He was feeling somewhat frustrated, for he had scorned the superior comforts of the Erol Palas Hotel at Söke and had hired himself a taxi back to Kushadasi the previous night, only to find that the *meltem* was kicking up such a swell in the harbour that he could not possibly get back on board the *Jack London*.) Yet the crowds were so thick and buzzing with life that we had quite a time of it keeping together, and we had to elbow our way forcibly towards the open-air restaurant overlooking the Roman Agora.

The port of Ephesus, founded by Ionian settlers in the eleventh century B.C., has suffered the same fate as the harbours of Miletus. Up to the Middle Ages, a canal still joined it to the retreating Aegean, but by now all the waterways to the city are irrevocably buried below the encroaching epidermis of silt. From where we sat, however, at bare wooden tables under the trees, looking across the Agora to the site of the abandoned harbour, the scene before our eyes was in other respects as though an older Ephesus had come to life again. The flagged footpath of the Arcadian Way was crowded with holidaymakers, and the high grass mound over-

199

looking it was decorated with a tapestry of picnic-parties. Hucksters, entertainers and candy-sellers lined the Way, the knife-edge of their patter cutting shrilly through the general din. Some of the salesmen were stocked with twentieth-century commodities, like bubble-gum and candy-floss, but apart from that the scene was one that St Paul would have recognized – or Heraclitus before him. Fashions in sweetmeats may change, but the sights, sounds and manners of a Bank Holiday fairground are much the same at modern Hampstead Heath or Ephesus as they have been since the beginning of history.

After lunch, we wandered among the crowd. Here a man was perched on top of a large water-butt, shouting over our heads as he demonstrated a series of conjuring-tricks with a glass of water. ('Now,' Michael translated, 'he says he's going to turn the water into wine.') Under the arches of the Byzantine city-walls, spits of meat were turning and people were crowding around to buy skewers of *kebab*. Away behind the open-air restaurant, we came out onto Marble Street, then climbed up the newly-excavated road past the Odeon and the tomb of St Luke towards the Magnesia Gate. Freshly unearthed, the façades of the grandiose buildings put up in the Roman Imperial era shone with an astonishing newness, and a fulsome inscription in honour of the Emperor Hadrian was as crisp and sharp as though it had only just been unveiled. We reached the limit of the excavations, somewhere near the Gate. Ahead of us was a rolling field, beneath which was buried still more of this extraordinary ruin. Beyond the field, the hillside was traversed by a newly-cut road leading up to the Panaya Kapulu – the site of the little house on the mountainside above Ephesus, where some people believe that the Virgin Mary spent the last years of her life.

We turned and looked back over the whole of ancient Ephesus. Clean white flagstones led downhill from where we stood; marble house-fronts faced onto the road; while street upon street beyond stretched down as far as the Agora and harbour on the left, and away to the right along the foot of Mount Pion towards the Byzantine citadel and basilica, more than a mile away. Even when empty of people, the ruins of

Ephesus are a monument to the life of the ancient world as impressive as the relics of the Forum at Rome itself. Today, crowded with villagers to the *Bairam* festivities, it provided an evocation of that vanished life more vivid than anything we could have imagined. It gave us some conception of what Delphi was like at the times of its own great festivals: some conception, also, of the Ephesus that St Paul knew. Suppose we only plunged back into the mêlée and shouted a few strategically-chosen heresies, we might soon whip the crowds into an ugly mood – ugly enough to send them streaming down the Arcadian Way, screaming at the tops of their voices their patriotic slogan, 'Great is Diana of the Ephesians! Great is Diana of the Ephesians!'

What an opportunity this should have been to get our film cameras out and turning – yet something held us back. When we had left Miletus the day before, the last goal of our journey had been reached, and all at once we were struck down by a kind of collective lassitude. After almost three months without a break, we could screw ourselves up to a certain pitch, but no more. Having locked all our equipment into the Renault on going to lunch, we could not now bring ourselves to unload it again and settle down to work. Besides, it *was* a Saturday afternoon; it *was* a holiday; and when had we last taken a day, let alone a real weekend off? From that moment on, the signs of strain prolonged near the limits of endurance became more and more evident. Fotis was itchy and irritable, anxious to get back not only to Maureen, but also to Greece – for the atmosphere of Turkey scarcely agreed with him. I myself was feeling very seedy, and by bedtime that night I was in the hands of a doctor at Izmir, suffering from some kind of bronchial complaint which was at least half the product of nervous stress. By the afternoon of the next day, it was June's turn: she retired to bed with the sore throat and high temperature of a twenty-four-hour Turkish influenza.

Before retiring to Izmir and our sickbeds, we had managed to fit in one last piece of work, downstream from Ephesus, near the estuary of the Lesser Menderes. We had dropped Helen and Michael off at Kushadasi, with instructions to fetch us a change of clothing from the boat. (This they were in fact unable to do, since the boatman managed neither to row them round the end of the pier – where the seas were still too steep – nor under it, where they were in danger of braining themselves on the concrete; so they gave up and returned to the shore drenched and defeated.) Half-way between Kushadasi and Ephesus, the road ran beside a wonderful stretch of primitive marshland, whose whole layout was evocative of some Middle Eastern creation-myth. The first mud of the new Earth was appearing above the softly rippling waters, and beyond them waved the line of reeds from which the great gods fashioned the first human habitations. It was the same moment at which, the previous day, we had seen the sun setting across the Great Meander: now the silhouette on the North-west horizon was that of Chios. As we filmed, a pair of white egrets flew across the setting sun. Feathery and shivering against the evening light, the tops of the rushes lining the nearest channel of the river divided the sky from the earth. A stork trod delicately among the water-buttercups, stopping from time to time to plunge the rapier of its beak, where some unfortunate frog tried in vain to hide in the dark waters of the marsh.

We straightened up and looked around. We should have to tie up some loose ends when we got back to Athens: otherwise, that was that. Inland, the deep yellow of the evening sunlight was picking out the citadel, the mosque and the ruins of the Roman theatre. The only sounds were the wind in the reeds and the *koax-koax* of the frogs. Soon (please God) we could begin allowing ourselves to relax.

*   *   *

We got back to Tigani a couple of days later, in the evening. At the quayside café, our friends were still sitting round their *ouzo*, doing their best to drown the *bouzouki* music from the loudspeakers with the noise of their argument. 'Good lord,' was our first unthinking reaction, 'What are those women doing, sitting around in public? Unveiled, too! . . .' Michael and Dhaskalis spot us walking along the quay: 'How are you doing?' they shout. 'Sit down. . . . Have a drink. . . . So they didn't shoot you, eh? You got back safely. . . .' Yes, we have got back safely after less than a week. . . . It seems incredible; but one week ago precisely we were sitting at this same café, having a farewell drink with this same group of friends. We hand the borrowed Turkish ensign back to Dhaskalis. He smiles broadly, nodding his head sideways and twitching his moustache, then rolls it up briskly and tucks it away in his pocket. Less than a week. . . . It had been like journeying into another century and back again.

Next day summer has come – temporarily at any rate. Along the quay, the sunlight strikes vertically down to the harbour floor. There it picks out the solitary relics of a winter's rubbish: old buckets, lengths of rope, chunks of cast iron, and the complacent fish, tailing their way lazily through the jetsam.

Last night's political argument, interrupted when the power station closed down at half-past-eleven, has started up again in the café. The Harbour Master evidently feels that his office requires him to defend established authority, and the others are baiting him:

'That Karamanlis isn't really a Greek.'

'What do you mean – not a Greek?' The Harbour Master makes a face like a llama.

'He's not really a Greek, he's a Macedonian.'

The llama spits superciliously: 'Well, a Macedonian's a Greek, isn't he – like any other?'

'He's a Macedonian, and he does everything for Macedonia; but what does he do for the islands?'

The Harbour Master raises his eyebrows, as though the Government's services to the islands are too well-known to need enumeration.

'Well, why doesn't he give us a good, deep harbour? As deep as Mykonos? Or come to that, as deep as Karlovasi?' So the bickering goes on. One Samos town against another, one island against another, one province against another: Greece, it seems, is as addicted as the USA to the politics of the pork-barrel.

After lunch I walk over Mount Castro for one last visit to the north end of the Tunnel, taking with me that flash-light borrowed once more from the photographer at Vathy. (This time he does not offer to accompany me.) On the crest of the mountain, the sun is at last really hot. I strip and walk on across the prickly heath, thankful for the comfort of its warmth on my tired skin. From here above Tigani, on the wall of Polycrates' fortifications, the whole of Ionia is spread out below me.

For the first time, I realize just how compact this area of the globe was. Our scientific tradition first saw the light in a region the size of an English county. Clazomenae, Teos, Colophon, Ephesus, Panionium, Samos, Priene, Miletus: even in those days, the towns of the Ionian confederacy lay within a few hours' journey of one another. Indeed, they were all within signalling-range: though some of the towns (like Priene) lay shielded by the slopes of the mountains, a string of signal-fires on the hilltops above them could have carried messages from one end of Ionia to the other in a few minutes. As for the web of sea-routes by which the towns were all linked, these converged fatefully – as Polycrates had seen – on that mile-wide strait at my feet.

June has taken the village taxi along to the foot of the Ayiades valley. Coming down from the tunnel, I meet her among the flowering oleanders, where the last arches of the Roman aqueduct stride above the dried-up stream-bed. Costas, the young taxi-driver, takes us to pay a courtesy-call on the officers in charge of the new airfield. By half-past-four we are back in town, and half-an-hour later we are off, on the first leg of our journey back to Athens, and so to England. Helpful to the last, Manoli the odd-job man manhandles the gangway on board, and stands waving from the quay as we cast loose and move forward on the anchor-chain. The Harbour Master and the Customs officer stand side by side, in postures of authority. As we move away the Harbour Master salutes, and the Customs officer slowly lifts one hand in a grave farewell. Michel is busy at the telegraph office, but Dhaskalis has ridden down on a bicycle in order to see us off. Moving away across the frying-pan of the harbour, we see him pedalling wildly round the quay towards the mole, steering with one hand and waving with the other. He passes in front of the hotel and shouts up at Plato, who is up a ladder with a paint-pot, adding a third dimension of shading to the capital letters of the name 'Hotel Pythagorion'. Now Dhaskalis has disappeared behind the fishing-boats on the slip, and Tom Crichton puts the diesel into gear. The *Jack London* is under power, pushing her way out along the length of Polycrates' mole, while Dhaskalis stands waving from the end. Clear of the frying-pan handle, we turn and set a course South of West, to pass round the headland beyond the Temple of Hera and inside the offshore islet of Samopoula. Before long Tigani shrinks into a memory. The pilgrimage is over.

11 · Out by the Back Door

Athens, May 19. We have made up our minds not to delay longer, and will leave tomorrow at any cost – five days earlier than our original plan. Filming all afternoon in Alex's studio: young *bouzouki* player, friend of Fotis, doing one of his own pieces – 'only too happy', so no copyright or royalty trouble. After it is all over, J. and I go off with F. for a drink-cum-snack, which prolongs itself and turns into all the supper we have strength for. 'There are two bars in Athens where you can meet interesting people,' says F. 'We call one "The Standing Intelligentsia" and the other "The Sitting Intelligentsia". Which would you prefer?' We choose to sit.

The expedition is breaking up. Michael has left for Istanbul, travelling on a Russian boat bound for Odessa. The *Jack London* is gone from its berth down at the Piraeus, and should by now be in the Gulf of Corinth. With it have gone Tom Crichton, as owner-captain, and Maureen, who has her summer's obligations as resident ship's cook. We take it in turns to order long sweet vermouths-and-soda, together with strips of dried octopus and meat-balls. Fotis and June are sworn brother-and-sister. From his inner pocket, he produces a bundle of freshly-printed enlargements: photographs of Maureen which he has taken during the voyage. Pausing to order another round of vermouths, he turns back and takes us into his confidence. 'In September,' he tells us, 'Maureen will be coming back to Athens and we plan to be together for good.' We fall on his neck, with love and congratulations. All he can say is: 'I am so very lucky.'

At last I begin to believe that we are *capable* of stopping. Now Fotis is talking to us about Greece and its problems. We know what his country means to him. He and a half-dozen of his friends are – and know they are – the solid core of documentary film-makers in Greece; and that (they feel) is where they belong. For if they do not show Greece and its life as it really is today, others will come from abroad and do it wrong. They have seen Basil Wright's *The Immortal*

Land and are disappointed. 'He sees only the old things,' F. complains; 'but we have to live in the twentieth century. Greece must travel the modern road, too: we cannot be forever remembering Socrates – we have our own salvation to work out, by ourselves.'

Fotis has always suspected June of only *pretending* to be English ('You are not phlegmatic enough') and the Mediterranean germs lying dormant within us both were about to show themselves. It took the whole of next morning to chew through the last red tape keeping us in Athens, but by three o'clock in the afternoon we had got away. During our weeks in Ionia and the Islands, the countryside had changed colour. Beyond Eleusis we turned right and climbed over the pass into Boeotia. All along the hillside the black scrub was now green, and down on the plain beyond the crops were already tall and golden. We drove on through Thebes and Levadhia bound for Chrysso. Midway between Levadhia and Arachova, the road crosses a stretch of rough heathland and comes face to face with the steep Eastern face of Parnassus. Here at the corner of the road is the hamlet of Korakolithos (that is to say Crowstone). We had time in hand, so we stopped for a cup of tea and sat looking across the valley at the mountain. The final incongruity was about to burst upon us.

We were ordering our second cups when there was a distant rasping sound, which grew into a roar followed by a squealing whoosh. A high-powered sports car shot past the front of the café, rounded the first of the corners up onto the heath and disappeared, unrecognizable in a cloud of dust and exhaust. A minute later the performance was repeated: then a third and a fourth, and two more in quick succession. We went out on to the road and saw another car approaching at high speed, a metal plate on its radiator bearing the words '6e *Rallye Akropolis*'. We got back into our own car and set off carefully in the opposite direction, away from Athens. Passing through the first gorge, we came down to the crossroads where the young Oedipus unwittingly struck down his own father. As we came to the road-junction, two more cars cornered noisily, and shot past us in the direction of Athens: above us, three or four more were visible, snaking their way down the winding traverse from Arachova and Parnassus.

From this point on, the journey was purgatory. The scene itself was tantalizingly attractive. The road wound in a hundred hair-pins along the face of the mountain: on either side, the steep slopes had been ploughed and hoed into careful plots, and the dead vines of winter had already thrown out long pink and green shoots. Where the soil was too poor or too precipitous to carry even vines or olives, the golden broom was in flower, turning the lower slopes of the mountain into a patchwork of emerald, umber and canary-yellow. But this agricultural paradise was *infested* (no other word will do) with automobiles. The climax, for us, came two miles before Arachova. Crawling at ten miles an hour along the very verge, with horn blowing, we approached yet another blind turning, when suddenly we were bounced by a string of three Triumphs (with British number-plates), skittering at top speed down the middle of the road, and engaged – it seemed – in their own private race. It was a choice between death and the ditch: instinctively I chose the ditch. June *thought* that the numbers on the sides of the cars had been 105, 106 and 107; but the whole incident was over in a flash, and by the time we were out of the car, cursing violently in our relief at being still alive, the predators were several hundred yards down the road and past identification.

Through good fortune we had met the ditch at a point where the bank was soft rather than rocky. In five minutes we had hauled ourselves back onto the road again, with only super-ficial damage to the car. More carefully than ever, we crept on – horn blaring – to Arachova, where we found the streets lined with enthusiastic crowds cheering the competitors through. We tried to register a protest: if a rally-driver forced a passing motorist into the ditch, surely he should lose some points – even if he didn't have the luck to kill him? Irony was lost on the organizing officials, and we gave up the attempt. The only thing was to go on as cautiously as we knew how, and to pray. Between Arachova and Delphi we had a slice of luck: a heavy truck was lumbering its way slowly through the olive-groves, blocking off more than half the road, and this induced respect even in the oncoming sports cars. Preferring life to speed, we took our place behind the truck, and were content to rely on it as our protective armour-plating.

We were just coming up past the museum at Delphi and were about to turn the corner into the village, when an olive-uniformed policeman stepped up and held out his hand, waving us into the side of the road. I stopped and asked what was up. We could not go on, he said, as the road was closed. Closed? I replied, what did he mean – closed? The road was closed, he repeated: we must stop and wait here. 'But we're only going as far as Chrysso,' we protested: 'we've only got two miles to go and our friends are expecting us.' He couldn't help that, the road was closed – surely we knew there was a rally on?

At the mention of the rally, I felt the first seditious stirrings within me. This was really adding insult to near-injury. Yes, I answered, we did indeed know there was a rally on: in fact, we wanted to lodge a formal complaint about the dangerous driving. Wasn't it enough to be driven into the ditch by those car-fiends, without being denied the chance of going our last two miles on their account? 'Ah!' he countered, smiling at the un-answerability of his own counter-argument, 'but there are *English* competitors taking part in the rally.' This irrelevant appeal to national pride only irked me the more. 'Yes, and it was English drivers who nearly killed us.' In any case, how long was the road closed for? He couldn't say – perhaps till eight, perhaps till nine, perhaps later – we must just wait here, as it was *closed*.

The fifth time he said it, something violent got loose inside me. A new and rebellious Mediterranean soul broke through the crust of my English habits. I lost my temper dramatically, noisily and blasphemously, shouting at him with a scorn and violence of which I did not know I was capable. He recoiled a step, on the defensive: English tourists were usually more amenable. I went on shouting at him, determined not to go on being 'a good guest', keeping in line and complying unquestioningly with his arbitrary orders. 'But the road is *closed*,' he bleated again. By this time, I no longer believed a word of it. From what I knew about rallies, I doubted whether the police in *any* country could legally close an essential main road such as this – the only road-link along the North side of the Gulf of Corinth. If the man produced some printed notice of closure, well and good. Meanwhile, I would go on making my scepticism angrily clear.

By this time, he was no longer so complacent. Driven to the point of embarrassment, he was trying to pacify me: '*Endaxi, endaxi* (all right, all right) . . .', he began; and at that my new Greek personality boiled over. This – I could see it now – was no London police-constable, correct, polite, always careful to act within his legal authority: this was, this was just . . . just a . . . *bogey*! '*Dhen einai endaxi*! (it's *not* all right)', I roared back at him, '*Einai Dhemotike e odhos* (it's a public road).' As my blood was rising, I had put the car into gear, and now I let in the clutch. The boil of my fury burst within me and, as the car jerked forward, I stuck my head out of the window and spat violently on the ground at the policeman's feet. (In reconstructing the story, I have written that 'I did' this, that and the other: at the time, it felt rather as though all these things were 'doing themselves' in and through me.)

The last stupefied fragment of Englishman shrank back into the corner of my mind, contemplating this display of wrath with as much astonishment as anyone else. 'You were wonderful,' June was saying as we turned the corner to enter the village; but at that moment a police-sergeant stepped out from the kerb, and we were held up once more. Now the row began again. He *told* us that the road was closed, but would show us neither notice nor authority. He was just *telling* us: we must wait till half-past-eight – with luck – or perhaps nine, before going on. I got out of the car and started to argue with him. June slipped quietly across into the driver's seat. Instead of trying to pacify us, the sergeant turned to threats, forming imitation handcuffs over his wrists with thumb and forefinger. Now things began to look really difficult, for at that moment the tall policeman whom I had previously insulted came up from behind and began asking for our passports. It was desirable (I thought) that my knowledge of modern Greek should evaporate at this point, for once we had handed over our passports we were done for. Deaf to the constable's requests, I kept on arguing with the sergeant, who finally admitted grudgingly that the rally organizers had a control-point in the village and gave us permission to go and register our protest.

June drove off ahead towards the Rally Control and, as soon as I could, I disengaged myself from the policeman and ran off after her: 'Get in quick,' she said. Twenty-five yards further on again, a third policeman diverted us up the side-road which leads through the back of the village and comes out (as I soon estimated) near the Tourist Hotel. 'That's fine,' I said, 'just keep going up here. Once we get to the Tourist Hotel, there's another lane on from it, which comes out on the main road, right the other side of the town.' Having got that far, we could surely make our way down the mile-and-a-half of open road to Chrysso and our friends. We reached the hotel, drove across the car park, and were out the other side. At the foot of the drive, where it debouched on to the main road, a string of four cars was waiting, with yet another policeman controlling the exit. June was reluctant to refuse at the last fence. She drove straight past the queue of cars, and when the policeman stepped out towards us, she stepped on the accelerator, waved gaily in the direction of Itea, and shouted through the window the single Greek word 'Ferimpot'. We were (she implied) in a hurry to catch the 'ferry-boat' across the Gulf of Corinth, so – alas! – we could not *stay*.

*   *   *

Waking next morning at Chrysso, we discovered that the time of the afternoon ferry to Aiyion had been changed. Now it did not leave until 4.30 p.m., so cutting our arrival at Patras rather fine, and we reconciled ourselves – happily enough – to driving across the mountains from Amphissa to Navpaktos and the Rion Narrows. The road from Amphissa climbed up through the last of the olive-groves to the bare shoulder of the hills. From the final hairpin, the whole amphitheatre of Parnassus was displayed below us for the last time: the bare, limestone-capped wall of the mountain stretched east to beyond Arachova, with Delphi perched on a col across the far side and, in the foreground to our left, the projecting spur carrying the monastery of the Prophet Elijah.

We went on over the top, past the turning to Galaxidhi, and down an inland valley to Lidhorikion. The tarmac ended, giving way to dust and earth, but the Citroen ran happily on the primitive road-surface and we kept up our speed. Beyond Lidhorikion we were in the valley of the Mornos, and had recognizably entered the Balkans. The earth track wound along the valley base, clambered from time to time around the spurs of the foothills to avoid a marsh, leapt side-streams and ducked under trees, never forgetting how recently it had been only a bridle-path. On either side of the river, there was a narrow strip of water-meadow. Beyond this, the hills rose steeply all the way, thickly wooded near the foot but gradually thinning out towards their summits. On the right, the slope swept on upwards to nearly 8,000 feet. On the left, a 5,000-foot ridge separated us from the Gulf of Corinth. Down in the valley there was scarcely a hamlet. The deep-green tranquillity of the place was heavy with silence, a preserve for fauns and wood-nymphs. We crossed a Bailey bridge and the road made its final effort, clambering 2,000 feet up to a ridge. As we wound our way upwards through the woods, an eagle floated across the road and out over the valley, circling lower and lower with an easy confidence that emphasized the remote loneliness of the place. Halfway up, a single goatherd stood in the ditch by the road – the only human being for miles – dressed in goatskin from neck to ankles, and chewing away at a piece of hard goat-cheese. Beyond the crest, the view opened out more widely to the South and West. Then yes: there it was – the sea. We ran down over the end of the ridge for the last dozen miles with the Gulf of Corinth in sight, across the mouth of the Mornos (suddenly grown broad) and into Navpaktos.

It was three in the afternoon but in the local *taverna*, under the plane-trees by the harbour, grilled fish could still be had from the charcoal brazier. Like some pocket Dubrovnik, Navpaktos – or Lepanto – keeps its Venetian walls and port. The fortifications are scribbled all over the lower hills behind and around the town, but the harbour itself is a miniature. Those 200 ill-fated Turkish galleys, which went out from here in October 1571 to be destroyed by Don John of Austria, could hardly (we decided) have started from *inside* the harbour: one could barely get 200 skiffs into a harbour that size. Presumably they assembled in the open Gulf, and then reached out through the 'little Dardanelles', between Rion and Andirrion, to their doom.

The road from Navpaktos to Andirrion ran between rich fields. On either side, the corn was already turning to gold, while away to the left, in the clear air of early summer, the waters of the Gulf were ultramarine. A light haze hung over the mountains of the Peloponnese. Along the edge of the fields, wild delphiniums and poppies varied the colour-scheme, and all the way along the road men, women, children, dogs and bicycles mingled together in a relaxed confusion. It was three months since that February morning when we first penetrated into the Gulf of Corinth from the West. Now this land was no longer foreign to us: the life being lived along this shore-line had become familiar, and it was the sea ahead of us which held unknown things in store. A cold South-westerly breeze was beating strongly up from Sicily and into the mouth of the Gulf. We ran on between the cornfields and down to the landing-stage at Andirrion. The ferryboat across the jaws of the Gulf was due to leave in twenty minutes. The circle of our journey had closed.

*   *   *

Acciaroli, May 25: We have come to rest at last, even if only for the inside of a week. The *Albergo Girasole* is a modest little hotel, but brand-new. It is early in the season, and we are the only guests, wandering down the pebble-path across the vegetable-garden to take up our monopoly of the sandy beach. Three months of unending activity and enforced society leave us with only one desire – to be immobile, and alone.

We are on the shore of the Cilento, the great coastal headland that separates Salerno from the Deep South. We came here by way of Brindisi and Taranto, across the instep of Italy and up over the mountains of Lucania, dropping down steeply to the West coast at the Gulf of Policastro. One hears much about the grinding poverty of Southern Italy but, after Greece, this looks like a land flowing with milk and

213

honey. The limestone skeleton of Greece has worn through the thin clothing of soil in a hundred places, but here even the hills are draped with thick forests of sweet chestnuts. If men are poor here, surely this must be largely a result of human improvidence and neglect, rather than a consequence of the sheer sterility of Nature.

In the ancient world, this coastal strip was part of Magna Graecia – the new world of colonies in the West, to which men could flee from the tyrannies and uncertainties of life in Asia Minor. Pythagoras visited Metapontum and settled at Croton, both of them on the Gulf of Taranto – close to Sybaris, whose reputation for luxury equalled that of Lydia and Croesus. Here on the West coast, between Acciaroli and Cape Palinuro (where Aeneas' steersman was washed ashore), there is a fertile valley protected by a ring of mountains, reminiscent of the plain of Argos. On the shore of this plain stood Elea, the home of Parmenides – the poet-metaphysician who stated the logical quandaries with which Plato and Aristotle were later preoccupied: probing that contrast between the eternal and the transitory which was to be a recurrent theme of all Greek philosophy.

After supper, we stay outdoors until sunset, then retire indoors to the bar and play cards with the country pack provided by the hotel (twelve cards to a suit – buttons, flowers, shovels and staves). Later, from the balcony outside our bedroom, we watch the last light fading out of the sky. In the mouth of the bay, a mile or more out, the fishing-boats have hung acetylene lamps over their bows and are waiting for the fish to rise. From where we stand, leaning on the rail of the balcony, the lights flicker on and off under their hoods, as the boats tilt and pitch – fleeting specks of light appearing and disappearing on the face of the dark sea, in absolute contrast to the relentless cycle of night and day.

In these self-sufficient villages of the Cilento, the old agri-cultural cycle of life pursues its time-tested course, dependent on the sequences of nature and in harmony with them. Down beside the road, the rope-makers are at work: they spin out the fibres, then roll and thread them together, twisting and plaiting them before stretching them (stre-e-etching them, as the advertisers would say) on a wooden frame, and finally 'walking' them round the roadside trees to give them suppleness.

The intellectual upheavals of the sixteenth and seventeenth

century (one must remember) were preceded by an another, agricultural revolution, whose instrument was the heavy iron plough. With iron, men cleared the forests of Northern Europe, and broke up the rain-soaked clods. With iron, they learned to manipulate Nature and impose their will on her, so that she became their servant instead of their senior partner. In the path of the iron plough, a new focus of civilization arose. Rainy but fertile, the countries of Northern Europe became a counterpoise to the sun-baked but thin-soiled Mediterranean lands.

The boundary between the old and the new ran across the Plain of Lombardy, and helped to make Venice and its neighbours the Ionia of the Renaissance. At Padua were conceived the crucial concepts of the new mechanical view of nature – Galileo's theory of motion, and the anatomical method of Fabricius and Harvey. New modes of thought sprang from new modes of living: new intellectual concepts emerged in the context of new *forms of life* – the phrase is Wittgenstein's. It was not that changes in the economic basis of society forced new theories on the science of the Renaissance: in this sort of situation economic forms, too, are 'carts' as much as 'horses'. Rather the whole scope of human endeavour and understanding took a major step onwards. The ancient goal of living in harmony with Nature, and of comprehending man's place in the cycles of Heaven and Earth, was joined by – and beginning to give way to – another aim: that of rising above the limitations of terrestrial Nature, and exploiting the mechanical principles underlying all her operations to serve Man's own ends.

Our journey had taught us one thing at least. The ancient habits of life still survive into the twentieth century, and one can, with a little effort, place oneself back within them. From this older point of view, one can look at the world of Nature with the eyes of the ancient Greeks; and by doing so one comes to recognize that their fundamental concepts represent, not elementary fallacies, but an intelligible and justifiable system of thought. Now, however, it was time to leave the lands where a life of contentment – if not of opulence – can be lived merely by co-operating with the processes of Nature; and to return to the cold and mechanical North, where one must either master Nature, or be mastered by her.

We set off along the smiling *corniche* of the Northern Cilento and turned inland across a country drenched with golden broom, through Agropoli (what echoes did that name awaken?) and on towards the main road joining Naples to Sicily. Near the point where our winding coastal road was swallowed up into this North-South highway, we stopped for the last time. Side by side in a green lawn, there stood three ancient temples of perfect Doric simplicity – each of them among the very finest in the whole Greek world. This was Paestum. In the innocence of my imagination, these temples had existed always in the fictional loneliness of a deserted moorland. But no: here the new world is treading closely on the heels of the old, and the ancient constellations are sinking to the horizon. All along the Western boundary of the sacred enclosure, separated from it only by a fence of wire-mesh, runs the tarmac ribbon of the *Strada Nazionale*.

We had started from Acciaroli very early, and when we reached Paestum the gates of the enclosure were still locked. We pulled the car off the road beside a café and breakfasted while waiting for the custodian to arrive and open up. Outside the fence, the cars and trucks sped up and down the highway, few of their occupants pausing to glance through the fence at this fragment of antiquity. Even we ourselves were beginning to have itchy feet. For one final half-hour we wandered among the ruins, trying to lose ourselves again in that older mode of existence. But the spell had been broken. We got back into the car, pulled out into the road, and launched ourselves onto the conveyor-belt of north-bound traffic.

Index

Index

221